COMPLEX ANALYSIS

UNIT A4 DIFFERENTIATION

Prepared by the Course Team

Before working through this text, make sure that you have read the
Course Guide for M337 Complex Analysis.

The Open University, Walton Hall, Milton Keynes, MK7 6AA.

First published 1993. Reprinted 1995, 1998, 2001, 2008

Edited, designed and typeset by the Open University using the Open University T$_{\text{E}}$X System.

Printed in Malta by Gutenberg Press Limited.

ISBN 0 7492 2178 X

This text forms part of an Open University Third Level Course. If you would like a copy of
Studying with The Open University, please write to the Central Enquiry Service,
PO Box 200, The Open University, Walton Hall, Milton Keynes, MK7 6YZ. If you have not
already enrolled on the Course and would like to buy this or other Open University material,
please write to Open University Educational Enterprises Ltd, 12 Cofferidge Close, Stony
Stratford, Milton Keynes, MK11 1BY, United Kingdom.

1.4

CONTENTS

Introduction   4

    Study guide   5

1 Derivatives of Complex Functions   6

    1.1 The definition of derivative   6

    1.2 The Combination Rules   8

    1.3 Non-differentiability   11

    1.4 Higher-order derivatives   14

    1.5 A geometric interpretation of derivatives   14

2 The Cauchy–Riemann Equations   16

    2.1 The Cauchy–Riemann Theorems (audio-tape)   16

    2.2 Proofs   20

3 The Composition, Inverse and Restriction Rules   23

    3.1 The Composition Rule   23

    3.2 The Inverse Function Rule   27

    3.3 The Restriction Rule   29

    3.4 Standard functions   30

4 Smooth Paths   31

    4.1 Derivatives of parametrizations   31

    4.2 A geometric interpretation of derivatives (revisited)   35

    4.3 Conformal functions   36

Exercises   39

Solutions to the Problems   41

Solutions to the Exercises   46

INTRODUCTION

The derivative of a real function f at a point c is the slope of the tangent to the graph of f at c. This slope is calculated by finding the slope of the chord joining the point $(c, f(c))$ to a (nearby) point $(x, f(x))$, and taking the limit as x approaches c (Figure 0.1).

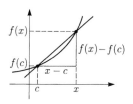

Figure 0.1

Now, the slope of the chord is equal to the ratio

$$\frac{f(x) - f(c)}{x - c}.$$

This ratio is often called the *difference quotient* for f at c, and its limit as x tends to c provides a formal definition of the (real) derivative of f at c, denoted by $f'(c)$. Thus

$$f'(c) = \lim_{x \to c} \frac{f(x) - f(c)}{x - c}.$$

In the case of complex functions, it is difficult to think about derivatives in terms of slopes of tangents, since the graph of a complex function is not drawn in two dimensions. Instead, we define the derivative of a complex function directly in terms of difference quotients, using the notion of complex limits discussed in the previous unit.

Fortunately, the derivatives of many complex functions turn out to have the same form as those of the corresponding real functions. For example, the derivative of the complex sine function is the complex cosine function, and the complex exponential function is its own derivative. On the other hand, the complex modulus function fails to be differentiable at every point of $\mathbb{C}$, even though the real modulus function (Figure 0.2) is differentiable at every point of $\mathbb{R} - \{0\}$. This reflects the fact that complex differentiation imposes a much stronger condition on functions than does real differentiation. Indeed, as the course progresses, you will see that differentiable complex functions have remarkably pleasant properties. For example, if a complex function can be differentiated once throughout a region, then it can be differentiated any number of times. There is no equivalent result for real functions.

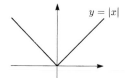

Figure 0.2   The real modulus function

In Section 1, we define *complex differentiation* and show how the definition can be used to establish whether a function is differentiable. By introducing the *Combination Rules*, we show how complex polynomial and rational functions can be differentiated just as in the real case. At the end of Section 1, we give a geometric interpretation of complex differentiation by introducing the idea of a complex scale factor.

In Section 2, we introduce the concept of *partial differentiation* for real functions of two real variables, and use it to establish a relationship between complex differentiation and real differentiation. This relationship sometimes enables us to differentiate a complex function using real derivatives. Indeed, at the end of the section we use this approach to show that the complex exponential function is its own derivative.

In Section 3, we introduce rules for differentiating composite and inverse functions, and show how they can be used to differentiate the principal logarithm and power functions. We also introduce a *Restriction Rule* that enables us to cut away unwanted parts from the domain of a function without affecting the differentiability of the function at the remaining points.

Finally, in Section 4, we concentrate on the derivatives of parametrizations of paths. We introduce the notion of a *smooth* path, and use it to pursue the geometric interpretation of derivative begun in Section 1. In particular, we show that a differentiable complex function preserves angles between paths.

Study guide

Sections 1 and 3 contain the complex versions of many results which will be familiar to you from your study of real differentiation. This should help you to remember the results. There are, however, important differences between real and complex differentiation, and you should study the sections with this in mind.

Section 2 is the audio-tape section. The only information that you will need to know from Section 2 in order to study Section 3 is that the complex exponential function is its own derivative.

The work on paths in Section 4 is important, and will be used throughout the course. In particular, it will be used in the next unit to define complex integration.

Associated with this unit is a segment of the Video Tape for the course. Although this unit text is self-contained, access to the video tape will enhance your understanding. Suitable points at which to view the video tape are indicated by a symbol placed in the margin.

1 DERIVATIVES OF COMPLEX FUNCTIONS

After working through this section, you should be able to:

(a) use the definition of *derivative* to show that a given function is differentiable, and to find its derivative;

(b) use the Combination Rules to differentiate polynomials and rational functions;

(c) use various strategies to show that a given function is not differentiable at a point;

(d) interpret the derivative of a complex function at a point as a rotation and a scaling of a small disc centred at the point.

1.1 The definition of derivative

As with limits and continuity, the way in which the derivative of a complex function is defined is similar to the real case. Thus a complex function is said to have a *derivative* at a point $\alpha \in \mathbb{C}$ if the **difference quotient**, defined by

$$\frac{f(z) - f(\alpha)}{z - \alpha},$$

tends to a limit as z tends to α. Equivalently, it is sometimes more convenient to replace z by $\alpha + h$, and examine the corresponding limit as h tends to 0. The difference quotient then has the form

$$\frac{f(\alpha + h) - f(\alpha)}{h},$$

where h is complex.

> **Definition** Let f be a complex function whose domain contains the point α. Then the **derivative of f at α** is
>
> $$\lim_{z \to \alpha} \frac{f(z) - f(\alpha)}{z - \alpha} \quad \left(\text{or} \ \lim_{h \to 0} \frac{f(\alpha + h) - f(\alpha)}{h} \right),$$
>
> provided that this limit exists. If it does exist, then f is **differentiable at α**. If f is differentiable at *every* point of a set A, then f is **differentiable on A**. A function is **differentiable** if it is differentiable on its domain.
>
> The derivative of f at α is denoted by $f'(\alpha)$, and the function
>
> $$f' : z \longmapsto f'(z)$$
>
> is called the **derivative of the function f**. The domain of f' is the set of all complex numbers at which f is differentiable.

The equivalence of these two limits can be justified by noting that, if $z = \alpha + h$, then '$z \to \alpha$' is equivalent to '$h \to 0$'.

The existence of these limits implicitly requires the domain of f to contain α as one of its limit points. This is necessarily satisfied if the domain of f is a region. (For the definition of limit point see *Unit A3*, Section 3.)

The function f' is sometimes called the **derived function** of f.

In Leibniz notation, $f'(z)$ is written as $\dfrac{df}{dz}(z)$ or $\dfrac{d}{dz}(f(z))$ if $f(z)$ is a complicated expression.

In some cases it is easy to find the derivative of a function directly from the above definition.

Example 1.1

Use the above definition to find the derivative of the function $f(z) = z^2$.

Solution

The domain of $f(z) = z^2$ is the whole of $\mathbb{C}$, so let α be an arbitrary point of $\mathbb{C}$. Then

$$f'(\alpha) = \lim_{z \to \alpha} \frac{f(z) - f(\alpha)}{z - \alpha} = \lim_{z \to \alpha} \frac{z^2 - \alpha^2}{z - \alpha} = \lim_{z \to \alpha} (z + \alpha).$$

By the Sum Rule for limits, it follows that $f'(\alpha) = \alpha + \alpha = 2\alpha$.

Since α is an arbitrary complex number, the derivative of f is the function $f'(z) = 2z$. Its domain is the whole of $\mathbb{C}$. ∎

Notice the way in which the troublesome $z - \alpha$ term cancels from the numerator and the denominator. This often happens when the definition is used to find derivatives.

Problem 1.1

Use the above definition to find the derivative of:

(a) the constant function $f(z) = 1$; (b) the function $f(z) = z$.

Problem 1.1 and Example 1.1 show that the functions $f(z) = 1$, $f(z) = z$ and $f(z) = z^2$ are differentiable on the whole of $\mathbb{C}$. Functions that have this property are given a special name.

> **Definition** A function is **entire** if it is differentiable on the whole of $\mathbb{C}$.

Not all functions are entire; indeed, many interesting aspects of complex analysis arise from functions that fail to be differentiable at various points of $\mathbb{C}$.

Problem 1.2

Use the definition to find the derivative of the function $f(z) = 1/z$. Explain why f is not entire.

Although the function $f(z) = 1/z$ is not entire, it is differentiable on the whole of its domain $\mathbb{C} - \{0\}$. This domain is a region because it is obtained by removing the point 0 from $\mathbb{C}$. As the course progresses you will discover that regions provide an excellent setting for analyzing the properties of differentiable functions. We therefore make the following definitions.

The removal of a point from a region leaves a region. (*Unit A3* Theorem 4.3)

> **Definition** A function that is differentiable on a region $\mathcal{R}$ is said to be **analytic on** $\mathcal{R}$. If the domain of a function f is a region, and if f is differentiable on its domain, then f is said to be **analytic**. A function is **analytic at a point** α if it is differentiable on a region containing α.

If a function is analytic on a region $\mathcal{R}$ then it is automatically analytic at each point of $\mathcal{R}$.

Notice that a function can have a derivative at a point without being analytic at the point. For example, in the next section we will ask you to show that the function $g(z) = |z|^2$ has a derivative at 0, but at no other point. This means that there is no region on which g is differentiable, and hence no point at which g is analytic. By contrast $f(z) = 1/z$ is analytic at every point of its domain. It is an analytic function, and it is analytic on *any* region that does not contain 0. Three such regions are illustrated in Figure 1.1.

An appropriate choice of region can often simplify the analysis of complex functions.

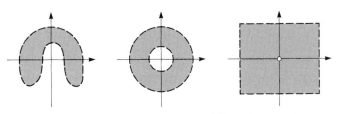

Figure 1.1 Three regions on which $f(z) = 1/z$ is analytic

Problem 1.3

Classify each of the following statements as True or False.

(a) An entire function is analytic at every point of $\mathbb{C}$.

(b) If a function is differentiable at each point of a set, then it is analytic on that set.

There is a close connection between differentiation and continuity. The function $f(z) = 1/z$, for example, is not only differentiable, but also continuous on its domain. This is no accident for, as in real analysis, *differentiability* implies *continuity*.

Theorem 1.1 If the complex function f is differentiable at α, then f is continuous at α.

Proof Let f be differentiable at α; then

$$\lim_{z \to \alpha} \frac{f(z) - f(\alpha)}{z - \alpha} = f'(\alpha).$$

To prove that f is continuous at α we will show that $f(z) \to f(\alpha)$ as $z \to \alpha$. We do this by proving the equivalent result that $f(z) - f(\alpha) \to 0$ as $z \to \alpha$.

See Theorem 3.1 of *Unit A3*.

By the Product Rule for limits, we have

$$\lim_{z \to \alpha} (f(z) - f(\alpha)) = \lim_{z \to \alpha} \left(\frac{f(z) - f(\alpha)}{z - \alpha} \right) \times \lim_{z \to \alpha} (z - \alpha) = f'(\alpha) \times 0 = 0.$$

Hence $f(z) \to f(\alpha)$ as $z \to \alpha$, and so f is continuous at α. ∎

In fact, differentiability implies more than continuity. Continuity asserts that, for all z close to α, $f(z)$ is close to $f(\alpha)$. For *differentiable* functions this 'closeness' has the 'linear' form described in the following theorem.

Theorem 1.2 Linear Approximation Theorem

If the complex function f is differentiable at α, then f may be approximated near α by a linear polynomial. More precisely,

$$f(z) = f(\alpha) + (z - \alpha)f'(\alpha) + e(z),$$

where e is an 'error function' satisfying $e(z)/(z - \alpha) \to 0$ as $z \to \alpha$.

'$e(z)/(z - \alpha) \to 0$ as $z \to \alpha$' means that '$e(z)$ tends to zero faster than $z - \alpha$'.

Proof We have to show that the function e defined by

$$e(z) = f(z) - f(\alpha) - (z - \alpha)f'(\alpha)$$

satisfies $e(z)/(z - \alpha) \to 0$ as $z \to \alpha$.

Dividing $e(z)$ by $z - \alpha$ and letting z tend to α, we obtain

$$\lim_{z \to \alpha} \frac{e(z)}{z - \alpha} = \lim_{z \to \alpha} \left(\frac{f(z) - f(\alpha)}{z - \alpha} - f'(\alpha) \right) = f'(\alpha) - f'(\alpha) = 0,$$

as required. ∎

Theorems 1.1 and 1.2 are often used to investigate the properties of differentiable functions. An illustration of this occurs in the next subsection, where Theorem 1.1 is used in the proof of the Combination Rules for differentiation. Later in this section we use Theorem 1.2 to give a geometric interpretation of complex differentiation.

1.2 The Combination Rules

It would be extremely tedious if we had to use the definition of the derivative every time we needed to differentiate a function. Fortunately, once the derivatives of simple functions like $z \longmapsto 1$ and $z \longmapsto z$ are known, we can find the derivatives of other more complicated functions by applying the following Combination Rules.

Theorem 1.3 Combination Rules

Let f and g be complex functions with domains A and B, respectively, and let α be a limit point of $A \cap B$. If f and g are differentiable at α, then

Sum Rule $f + g$ is differentiable at α and
$$(f + g)'(\alpha) = f'(\alpha) + g'(\alpha);$$

Multiple Rule λf is differentiable at α, for $\lambda \in \mathbb{C}$, and
$$(\lambda f)'(\alpha) = \lambda f'(\alpha);$$

Product Rule fg is differentiable at α, and
$$(fg)'(\alpha) = f'(\alpha)g(\alpha) + f(\alpha)g'(\alpha);$$

Quotient Rule f/g is differentiable at α (provided that $g(\alpha) \neq 0$), and
$$\left(\frac{f}{g}\right)'(\alpha) = \frac{g(\alpha)f'(\alpha) - f(\alpha)g'(\alpha)}{(g(\alpha))^2}.$$

If the domains A and B are regions, then every point of $A \cap B$ is a limit point of A and of B. (See Section 3 of *Unit A3* for the definition of limit point.)

In addition to these rules, there is a corollary of Theorem 1.3, known as the Reciprocal Rule, which is a special case of the Quotient Rule.

Corollary 1 Reciprocal Rule

Let f be a function which is differentiable at α. If $f(\alpha) \neq 0$, then $1/f$ is differentiable at α, and
$$\left(\frac{1}{f}\right)'(\alpha) = \frac{-f'(\alpha)}{(f(\alpha))^2}.$$

The proof of the Combination Rules uses the Combination Rules for limits, discussed in *Unit A3*. In the next example we illustrate the method by proving the Product Rule.

Example 1.2

Prove the Product Rule for differentiation.

Solution

Let $F = fg$. Then

$$\lim_{z \to \alpha} \frac{F(z) - F(\alpha)}{z - \alpha}$$

$$= \lim_{z \to \alpha} \frac{(f(z)g(z)) - (f(\alpha)g(\alpha))}{z - \alpha}$$

$$= \lim_{z \to \alpha} \frac{(f(z) - f(\alpha))g(z) + f(\alpha)(g(z) - g(\alpha))}{z - \alpha}$$

$$= \left(\lim_{z \to \alpha} \frac{f(z) - f(\alpha)}{z - \alpha}\right)\left(\lim_{z \to \alpha} g(z)\right) + f(\alpha)\left(\lim_{z \to \alpha} \frac{g(z) - g(\alpha)}{z - \alpha}\right)$$

$$= f'(\alpha)g(\alpha) + f(\alpha)g'(\alpha). \quad \blacksquare$$

Add and subtract $f(\alpha)g(z)$.

Sum, Product and Multiple Rules for limits.

g is differentiable, and hence continuous, at α, so
$$\lim_{z \to \alpha} g(z) = g(\alpha).$$

The proofs of the other Combination Rules are similar. We have asked you to prove the Sum and Multiple Rules in Problem 1.4. The proof of the Quotient Rule is left as an exercise (Exercise 1.2).

Problem 1.4

Prove the following rules for differentiation.

(a) The Sum Rule   (b) The Multiple Rule

The Combination Rules in Theorem 1.3 enable us to differentiate any polynomial or rational function. For example, since the function $f(z) = z$ is entire with derivative $f'(z) = 1$, we can repeatedly use the Product Rule to show that the function

$$f(z) = z^n \qquad (z \in \mathbb{C}),$$

is entire, and that its derivative is

$$f'(z) = nz^{n-1} \qquad (z \in \mathbb{C}).$$

Rational functions are quotients of polynomial functions (*Unit A2*, Subsection 1.3).

A formal proof of this result uses Mathematical Induction.

Next, we can use this fact, together with the Sum and Multiple Rules, to prove that any polynomial function is entire, and that its derivative is obtained by differentiating the polynomial function term by term. For example,

if $f(z) = 1 + 2z - 3z^2 + z^4$, then $f'(z) = 2 - 6z + 4z^3$.

In general, we have the following corollary to Theorem 1.3.

Corollary 2 Let p be the polynomial function

$$p(z) = a_0 + a_1 z + a_2 z^2 + \cdots + a_n z^n \qquad (z \in \mathbb{C}),$$

where $a_0, a_1, a_2, \ldots, a_n \in \mathbb{C}$ and $a_n \neq 0$. Then p is entire with derivative

$$p'(z) = a_1 + 2a_2 z + \cdots + na_n z^{n-1} \qquad (z \in \mathbb{C}).$$

Since a rational function is a quotient of two polynomial functions, it follows from Corollary 2 and the Quotient Rule that a rational function is differentiable at all points where its denominator is non-zero; that is, at all points of its domain.

Example 1.3

Find the derivative of

$$f(z) = \frac{2z^2 + z}{z^2 + 1},$$

and specify the domain of f'.

Solution

By Corollary 2, the derivative of

$$z \longmapsto 2z^2 + z \quad \text{is} \quad z \longmapsto 4z + 1,$$

and the derivative of

$$z \longmapsto z^2 + 1 \quad \text{is} \quad z \longmapsto 2z.$$

Provided that $z^2 + 1$ is non-zero, we can apply the Quotient Rule to obtain

$$f'(z) = \frac{(z^2 + 1)(4z + 1) - (2z^2 + z)(2z)}{(z^2 + 1)^2} = \frac{-z^2 + 4z + 1}{(z^2 + 1)^2}.$$

Since $z^2 + 1$ is non-zero everywhere apart from i and $-i$, it follows that the domain of f' is $\mathbb{C} - \{i, -i\}$. ∎

Problem 1.5

Find the derivative of each of the following functions. In each case, specify the domain of the derivative.

(a) $f(z) = z^4 + 3z^3 - z^2 + 4z + 2$ (b) $f(z) = \dfrac{z^2 - 4z + 2}{z^2 + z + 1}$

So, any rational function is differentiable on the whole of its domain. What is more, this domain must be a region because it is obtained by removing a finite number of points (zeros of the denominator) from $\mathbb{C}$.

Corollary 3 Any rational function is analytic.

A particularly simple example of a rational function is $f(z) = 1/z^n$, where n is a positive integer. This can be differentiated by means of the Reciprocal Rule:

$$f'(z) = \frac{-nz^{n-1}}{(z^n)^2} = -nz^{-n-1}.$$

If k is used to denote the negative integer $-n$, then we can write: $f(z) = z^k$ and $f'(z) = kz^{k-1}$. In this form it is apparent that the formula for differentiating a negative integer power is the same as the formula for differentiating a positive integer power. The only difference is that, for negative powers, 0 is excluded from the domain. We state these observations as a final corollary of Theorem 1.3.

Corollary 4 Let $k \in \mathbb{Z} - \{0\}$; then $f(z) = z^k$ has derivative $f'(z) = kz^{k-1}$. The domain of f' is $\mathbb{C}$ if $k > 0$ and $\mathbb{C} - \{0\}$ if $k < 0$.

1.3 Non-differentiability

In Theorem 1.1 you saw that *differentiability* implies *continuity*. An immediate consequence of this is the following test for non-differentiability.

Strategy A for non-differentiability

If f is discontinuous at α, then f is not differentiable at α.

Example 1.4

Show that there are no points of the negative real axis at which the function $f(z) = \sqrt{z}$ is differentiable.

Solution

In *Unit A3*, Problem 2.8 you saw that the function $f(z) = \sqrt{z}$ is discontinuous at all points of the negative real axis. It follows that there are no points of the negative real axis at which f is differentiable. ■

Problem 1.6 _____

Show that there are no points of the negative real axis at which the principal logarithm function

$$\text{Log} : z \longmapsto \log_e |z| + i \operatorname{Arg} z$$

is differentiable.

The converse of Theorem 1.1 is not true; if a function is continuous at a point, it does not follow that it is differentiable at the point. A particularly striking illustration of this is provided by the modulus function $f(z) = |z|$. This is continuous on the whole of $\mathbb{C}$ and yet, as you will see, it fails to be differentiable at each point of $\mathbb{C}$.

You showed that $f(z) = |z|$ is continuous on $\mathbb{C}$ in *Unit A3*, Frame 5.

Since $f(z) = |z|$ is continuous, Strategy A cannot be used to show that f fails to be differentiable at a given point α. Instead, we return to the definition of derivative and explain why the difference quotient for f fails to have a limit.

In general, if the domain A of a function f contains α as one of its limit points, then existence of the limit

$$\lim_{z \to \alpha} \frac{f(z) - f(\alpha)}{z - \alpha}$$

means that, for each sequence $\{z_n\}$ in $A - \{\alpha\}$ converging to α,

$$\lim_{n \to \infty} \frac{f(z_n) - f(\alpha)}{z_n - \alpha}$$

For the definition of limit of a sequence, see *Unit A3*, Section 1.

exists, and has a value which is independent of the sequence $\{z_n\}$. So, if two such sequences, $\{z_n\}$ and $\{z_n'\}$, can be found for which

$$\lim_{n \to \infty} \frac{f(z_n) - f(\alpha)}{z_n - \alpha} \neq \lim_{n \to \infty} \frac{f(z_n') - f(\alpha)}{z_n' - \alpha},$$

then f cannot be differentiable at α.

See the strategy for the non-existence of limits in Subsection 3.1 of *Unit A3*.

Example 1.5

Prove that $f(z) = |z|$ is not differentiable at 0.

Solution

We need to find two sequences $\{z_n\}$ and $\{z_n'\}$ converging to 0 which, when substituted into the difference quotient, yield sequences with different limits. A simple choice is to pick sequences $\{z_n\}$ and $\{z_n'\}$ that approach 0 along the real axis; one from the left, and one from the right.

There is no point in picking sequences that are more complicated than they need to be, so let $z_n = 1/n, n = 1, 2, \ldots$. Then

$$\lim_{n \to \infty} \frac{|z_n| - |0|}{z_n - 0} = \lim_{n \to \infty} \frac{1/n}{1/n} = 1.$$

Now let $z_n' = -1/n, n = 1, 2, \ldots$. Then

$$\lim_{n \to \infty} \frac{|z_n'| - |0|}{z_n' - 0} = \lim_{n \to \infty} \frac{1/n}{-1/n} = -1.$$

Since the two limits do not agree, the difference quotient does not have a limit as z tends to 0. It follows that $f(z) = |z|$ is *not* differentiable at 0. ∎

Since the real modulus function is not differentiable at 0, this result should not surprise you. Indeed the proof is identical to the real case.

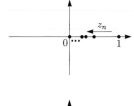

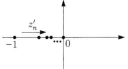

Figure 1.2

The next problem asks you to extend the method used in the above example to show that $f(z) = |z|$ is not differentiable at *every* point of $\mathbb{C}$.

Problem 1.7

Let α be any non-zero complex number, and consider the circle through α centred at the origin. By choosing one sequence $\{z_n\}$ that approaches α along the circumference of the circle, and another sequence $\{z_n'\}$ that approaches α along its radius (Figure 1.3), prove that $f(z) = |z|$ is not differentiable at α.

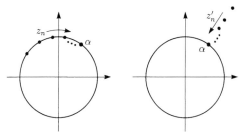

Figure 1.3

The modulus function illustrates an important difference between real and complex differentiation. When the modulus function is treated as a *real* function, the limit of its difference quotient has to be taken along the real line. But when treated as a *complex* function, the limit of the difference quotient is required to exist however the limit is taken. This explains why the real modulus function is differentiable at all non-zero real points, whereas the complex modulus function fails to be differentiable at each point of $\mathbb{C}$. More generally it shows that complex differentiability is a much stronger condition than real differentiability.

In Problem 1.7 you were able to prove that the modulus function failed to be differentiable by observing that its behaviour along the circumference of a circle centred at 0 is different from its behaviour along the radius. Similar observations can be applied to other functions. For example, in the next problem you may find it helpful to notice that directions of paths parallel to the imaginary axis are reversed by the function $f(z) = \overline{z}$, whereas the directions of paths parallel to the real axis are left unchanged (Figure 1.4).

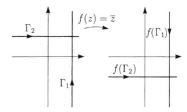

Figure 1.4

Problem 1.8

Show that there are no points of $\mathbb{C}$ at which the complex conjugate function $f(z) = \overline{z}$ is differentiable.

For some functions, you may be able to find a convergent sequence which yields a divergent sequence when substituted into the difference quotient. In such cases there is no need to look for a second sequence.

See the strategy for the non-existence of limits in Subsection 3.1 of *Unit A3*.

Example 1.6

Show that the function $f(z) = \sqrt{z}$ is not differentiable at 0.

Solution

We look for a sequence converging to 0 which yields a divergent sequence when substituted into the difference quotient. To make the square roots easy to handle, let $z_n = 1/n^2$. Then

$$\frac{f(z_n) - f(0)}{z_n - 0} = \frac{\sqrt{1/n^2} - \sqrt{0}}{1/n^2 - 0} = n.$$

Notice that Strategy A cannot be used here, since f is continuous at 0.

This sequence tends to infinity, and is therefore divergent. It follows that f is not differentiable at 0. ∎

The methods exemplified above for showing that a function is not differentiable at a given point may be summarized as follows.

Strategy B for non-differentiability

To prove that a function f is not differentiable at α, apply the strategy for the non-existence of limits to the difference quotient

$$\frac{f(z) - f(\alpha)}{z - \alpha}.$$

Subsection 3.1, *Unit A3*

If you think that a given function is *not* differentiable, then you should try to apply Strategy A or Strategy B above. If, on the other hand, you think that the function *is* differentiable, then you should try to find the derivative.

A third method of proving that f is not differentiable at a point appears in Frame 8 of the audio tape.

Problem 1.9

Decide whether each of the following functions is differentiable at i. If it is, then find its derivative at i.

(a) $f(z) = \operatorname{Re} z$ (b) $f(z) = 2z^2 + 3z + 5$ (c) $f(z) = \begin{cases} z, & \operatorname{Re} z < 0 \\ 4, & \operatorname{Re} z \geq 0 \end{cases}$

1.4 Higher-order derivatives

In Problem 1.2 you saw that the function $f(z) = 1/z$ has derivative $f'(z) = -1/z^2$, a result that you can also obtain using the Reciprocal Rule. If you now apply the Reciprocal Rule to the derivative $f'(z) = -1/z^2$, you obtain the following function:

$$(f')'(z) = \frac{2}{z^3} \qquad (z \neq 0).$$

A function of the form $(f')'$ is called the **second derivative of f**, and is denoted by f''. Continued differentiation gives the so-called **higher-order derivatives of f**. These are denoted by $f'', f''', f'''', \ldots$, and the values $f''(\alpha), f'''(\alpha), f''''(\alpha), \ldots$, are called the **higher-order derivatives of f at α**. Since the dashes in this notation can be rather cumbersome, we often indicate the order of the derivative by a number in brackets. Thus $f^{(2)}, f^{(3)}, f^{(4)}, \ldots$, mean the same as $f'', f''', f'''', \ldots$, respectively.

The brackets in $f^{(4)}$ are needed to avoid confusion with the fourth power of f.

When we wish to discuss a derivative of general order, we shall refer to the **nth derivative $f^{(n)}$ of f**. It is often possible to find a formula for the nth derivative in terms of n. For example, if $f(z) = 1/z$, then it is easy to see that

$$f''(z) = \frac{2}{z^3}, \quad f'''(z) = \frac{-2 \times 3}{z^4}, \quad f^{(4)}(z) = \frac{2 \times 3 \times 4}{z^5}, \quad \ldots,$$

and so the nth derivative is given by

$$f^{(n)}(z) = \frac{(-1)^n n!}{z^{n+1}}.$$

This can be proved by Mathematical Induction.

One interesting feature about this formula is that the domain $\mathcal{R} = \mathbb{C} - \{0\}$ remains the same, no matter how often the function f is differentiated. This is a special case of a much more general result which states that: *a function which is analytic on a region $\mathcal{R}$ has derivatives of all orders on $\mathcal{R}$*. We shall establish this remarkable fact and explore it in more detail in Block B, but for the rest of this unit we confine our attention to first-order derivatives. We continue to do this in the next subsection by giving a geometric interpretation of the first derivative.

1.5 A geometric interpretation of derivatives

As we mentioned in the Introduction, the derivative of a *real* function is often pictured geometrically as the slope of the graph of the function. This interpretation is very useful in real analysis, but is of little use in complex analysis, since the graph of a complex function is not two-dimensional.

Fortunately, there is another way of interpreting derivatives that works for complex functions. If a complex function f is differentiable at a point α, then any point z close to α is mapped by f to a point $f(z)$ close to $f(\alpha)$. Indeed, by the Linear Approximation Theorem,

$$f(z) = f(\alpha) + (z - \alpha)f'(\alpha) + e(z),$$

where $e(z)/(z - \alpha) \to 0$ as

So if $f'(\alpha) \neq 0$, then, $z \to \alpha$, *to a close approximation,*

$$f(z) - f(\alpha) \cong f'(\alpha)(z - \alpha).$$

The geometric interpretation is more complicated if $f'(\alpha) = 0$.

Multiplication of $z - \alpha$ by $f'(\alpha)$ has the effect of scaling $z - \alpha$ by the factor $|f'(\alpha)|$ and rotating it about 0 through the angle $\operatorname{Arg} f'(\alpha)$ — see Figure 1.5. Now consider $z - \alpha$ as the vector pointing from α to z (as shown on the left in Figure 1.6). Multiplication by $f'(\alpha)$ has the effect of scaling this vector by the factor $|f'(\alpha)|$ and rotating it through the angle $\operatorname{Arg} f'(\alpha)$. If we base the resulting vector at $f(\alpha)$, the image of α, we get (approximately) the vector $f(z) - f(\alpha)$ (see Figure 1.6). It follows that, to a close approximation, a complex derivative can be interpreted as a *complex scale factor* causing both a scaling (as for real scale factors) and a rotation.

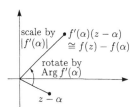

Figure 1.5

This geometric interpretation of complex multiplication was discussed in *Unit A1*.

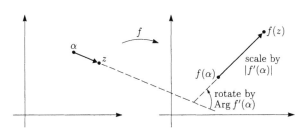

Figure 1.6   Interpreting a derivative as a scale factor

You may find it helpful to visualize a complex function f as a deformation of an elastic sheet representing the complex plane. The sheet is deformed so that each point α ends up at the point $f(\alpha)$. For most functions, this results in considerable distortions of the sheet. Locally, however, things appear somewhat simpler. Thus if f is analytic at α, and if $f'(\alpha) \neq 0$, then a small disc centred at α is mapped (approximately) to a small disc centred at $f(\alpha)$. In the process, the disc rotates through the angle $\operatorname{Arg} f'(\alpha)$, and is scaled by the factor $|f'(\alpha)|$ (see Figure 1.7).

As usual the rotation is anticlockwise if $\operatorname{Arg} f'(\alpha)$ is positive, and clockwise if it is negative.

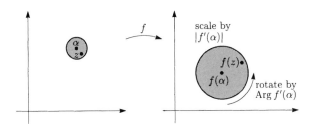

Figure 1.7   The approximate image of a disc, centred at a point α where $f'(\alpha) \neq 0$

Example 1.7

Using the notion of complex scale factor, describe what happens to points close to $1 + i$ under the function $f(z) = 1/z$.

Solution

To a close approximation, a small disc centred at $1 + i$ is mapped by f to a small disc centred at

$$f(1 + i) = 1/(1 + i) = \tfrac{1}{2}(1 - i).$$

In the process, the disc is scaled by the factor $|f'(1 + i)|$ and rotated through the angle $\operatorname{Arg} f'(1 + i)$.

Now $f'(z) = -1/z^2$, so

$$f'(1 + i) = \frac{-1}{(1 + i)^2} = \frac{-1}{2i} = \tfrac{1}{2}i,$$

which has modulus $\tfrac{1}{2}$ and principal argument $\pi/2$.

So f scales the disc by the factor $\tfrac{1}{2}$ and rotates it anticlockwise through the angle $\pi/2$. ■

Problem 1.10 _____

Using the notion of complex scale factor, describe what happens to points close to i under the function $f(z) = \dfrac{4z + 3}{2z^2 + 1}$.

___

It is important to bear in mind that the scale factor interpretation is only an approximation, and that it is unlikely to be reliable very far from the point under consideration. In the final section of this unit, we return to the scale factor interpretation and show how it can be described more precisely.

2 THE CAUCHY–RIEMANN EQUATIONS

After working through this section, you should be able to:

(a) find the *partial derivatives* of a function from $\mathbb{R}^2$ to $\mathbb{R}$;

(b) use the Cauchy–Riemann equations to show that a function is *not* differentiable at a given point;

(c) use the Cauchy–Riemann equations to show that a function, such as the exponential function, *is* differentiable at a given point, and to find the derivative.

2.1 The Cauchy–Riemann Theorems (audio-tape)

In this audio-tape section, we explore the relationship between complex differentiation and real differentiation. To do this, we introduce the notion of a *partial derivative* and use it to derive the *Cauchy–Riemann equations*. These equations are conditions that any differentiable complex function must satisfy, and so they can be used to test whether a given complex function is differentiable. In particular, we use them to investigate the differentiability of the complex exponential function. The technique is to split the exponential function into its real and imaginary part functions:

$$u(x, y) = e^x \cos y \quad \text{and} \quad v(x, y) = e^x \sin y.$$

In *Unit A2* the symbols u and v were used to denote variables. The use of the same symbols to represent functions should not cause confusion.

The derivative of exp is then calculated by using the derivatives of the *real* trigonometric and exponential functions, which we assume to be known.

In the audio tape we begin by exploring these ideas in the context of the function $f(z) = z^3$, so you may find it helpful to work through the following problem. The solution appears at the top of Frame 1.

Problem 2.1 _____

Find the real and imaginary part functions $u = \operatorname{Re} f$ and $v = \operatorname{Im} f$ for the function $f(z) = z^3$.

___

NOW START THE TAPE.

1. Real and imaginary parts of $f(z)=z^3$

solution to Problem 2.1

$u = \text{Re } f$
$v = \text{Im } f$

$f(x+iy) = (x+iy)^3$
$= (x^3 - 3xy^2) + i(3x^2y - y^3)$

$u(x,y) = x^3 - 3xy^2 \qquad v(x,y) = 3x^2y - y^3$

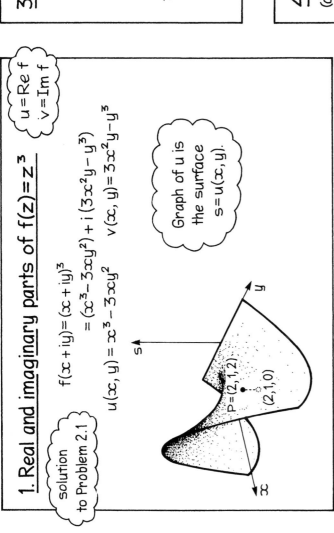

Graph of u is the surface $s = u(x,y)$.

$P = (2,1,2)$
$(2,1,0)$

---

2. Slope at P in x-direction (y fixed)

$u(x,y) = x^3 - 3xy^2$

so

$\dfrac{\partial u}{\partial x}(x,y) = 3x^2 - 3y^2$

$\dfrac{\partial u}{\partial x}(2,1) = 9$

Keep y fixed

partial derivative with respect to x

plane $y=1$

$\dfrac{\partial u}{\partial x}(a,b)$ is the derivative of $x \longrightarrow u(x,b)$ at a.

---

3. Slope at P in y-direction (x fixed)

$u(x,y) = x^3 - 3xy^2$

so

$\dfrac{\partial u}{\partial y}(x,y) = -6xy$

$\dfrac{\partial u}{\partial y}(2,1) = -12$

Keep x fixed.

partial derivative with respect to y

plane $x=2$

$\dfrac{\partial u}{\partial y}(a,b)$ is the derivative of $y \longrightarrow u(a,y)$ at b.

---

4. Problem 2.2

(a) Calculate the partial derivatives of
$v(x,y) = 3x^2y - y^3$.

(b) Evaluate these derivatives at $(2,1)$.

Compare with Frames 2 and 3.

---

5. Cauchy–Riemann Theorem

If f is differentiable at $\alpha = a + ib$,

then $\dfrac{\partial u}{\partial x}, \dfrac{\partial u}{\partial y}, \dfrac{\partial v}{\partial x}, \dfrac{\partial v}{\partial y}$ exist at (a,b) and

$$\dfrac{\partial u}{\partial x}(a,b) = \dfrac{\partial v}{\partial y}(a,b)$$

$$\dfrac{\partial v}{\partial x}(a,b) = -\dfrac{\partial u}{\partial y}(a,b)$$

$f: \mathcal{R} \to \mathbb{C}$
$u = \text{Re} f, \; v = \text{Im} f$
$\alpha \in \mathcal{R}$

Cauchy–Riemann equations

6. Derivative of f

$f(z) = u(x, y) + iv(x, y)$

$$f'(\alpha) = \lim_{z \to \alpha} \frac{f(z) - f(\alpha)}{z - \alpha} = \lim_{n \to \infty} \frac{f(z_n) - f(\alpha)}{z_n - \alpha} \qquad \left(z_n \to \alpha \text{ in } \mathcal{R} - \{\alpha\} \right)$$

If $z_n = x_n + iy_n$, $\alpha = a + ib$, then

$$\frac{f(z_n) - f(\alpha)}{z_n - \alpha} = \left[\frac{u(x_n, y_n) - u(a, b)}{(x_n - a) + i(y_n - b)} \right] + i \left[\frac{v(x_n, y_n) - v(a, b)}{(x_n - a) + i(y_n - b)} \right]$$

7. Special sequences $z_n \to \alpha$

$\alpha = a + ib$

Take $z_n = x_n + ib$, with $x_n \to a$:

$$\frac{f(z_n) - f(\alpha)}{z_n - \alpha} = \left[\frac{u(x_n, b) - u(a, b)}{x_n - a} \right] + i \left[\frac{v(x_n, b) - v(a, b)}{x_n - a} \right]$$

$$f'(\alpha) = \frac{\partial u}{\partial x}(a, b) + i\frac{\partial v}{\partial x}(a, b)$$

Take $z_n = a + iy_n$, with $y_n \to b$:

$$\frac{f(z_n) - f(\alpha)}{z_n - \alpha} = \left[\frac{u(a, y_n) - u(a, b)}{i(y_n - b)} \right] + i \left[\frac{v(a, y_n) - v(a, b)}{i(y_n - b)} \right]$$

$$f'(\alpha) = \left[\frac{1}{i}\frac{\partial u}{\partial y}(a, b) \right] + i \left[\frac{1}{i}\frac{\partial v}{\partial y}(a, b) \right]$$

$$f'(\alpha) = \frac{\partial v}{\partial y}(a, b) - i\frac{\partial u}{\partial y}(a, b)$$

Comparing boxes yields the Cauchy–Riemann equations.

Frame 5

8. Non-differentiability test

Let $f(x + iy) = u(x, y) + iv(x, y)$. If either

$$\frac{\partial u}{\partial x}(a, b) \neq \frac{\partial v}{\partial y}(a, b) \qquad \text{or} \qquad \frac{\partial v}{\partial x}(a, b) \neq -\frac{\partial u}{\partial y}(a, b),$$

then f is not differentiable at $a + ib$.

9. Where is $f(x + iy) = (x^2 + y^2) + i(2x + 4y)$ differentiable?

$u(x, y) = x^2 + y^2 \qquad v(x, y) = 2x + 4y$

$\dfrac{\partial u}{\partial x}(x, y) = 2x \qquad \dfrac{\partial v}{\partial x}(x, y) = 2$

$\dfrac{\partial u}{\partial y}(x, y) = 2y \qquad \dfrac{\partial v}{\partial y}(x, y) = 4$

(equal, only if $x = 2$)

(minus, only if $y = -1$)

Hence f fails to be differentiable at all points of $\mathbb{C} - \{2 - i\}$.

What happens at $2 - i$?

10. Problem 2.3

Show that each of the following functions fails to be differentiable at all points of $\mathbb{C}$.

(a) $f(x + iy) = e^x - ie^y$ \qquad (b) $f(z) = \bar{z}$

13. Is $f(x+iy) = (x^2+y^2) + i(2x+4y)$ differentiable at $2-i$?

$u(x,y) = x^2 + y^2$ $v(x,y) = 2x + 4y$

$\dfrac{\partial u}{\partial x}(x,y) = 2x$ $\dfrac{\partial v}{\partial x}(x,y) = 2$ (minus if $y = -1$)

$\dfrac{\partial u}{\partial y}(x,y) = 2y$ $\dfrac{\partial v}{\partial y}(x,y) = 4$ (equal if $x = 2$)

Partial derivatives are continuous; e.g. $\dfrac{\partial u}{\partial x}$ is $z \longmapsto 2\,\mathrm{Re}\,z$.

Hence f is differentiable at $2-i$, and

$$f'(2-i) = \frac{\partial u}{\partial x}(2,-1) + i\,\frac{\partial v}{\partial x}(2,-1) = 4 + 2i.$$

14. Where is $f(z) = e^z$ differentiable?

$u(x,y) = e^x \cos y$ $v(x,y) = e^x \sin y$

$\dfrac{\partial u}{\partial x}(x,y) = e^x \cos y$ $\dfrac{\partial v}{\partial x}(x,y) = e^x \sin y$ (minus)

$\dfrac{\partial u}{\partial y}(x,y) = -e^x \sin y$ $\dfrac{\partial v}{\partial y}(x,y) = e^x \cos y$ (equal)

Partial derivatives are continuous; e.g. $\dfrac{\partial u}{\partial x}$ is $z \longmapsto e^{\mathrm{Re}\,z}\cos(\mathrm{Im}\,z)$.

Hence f is differentiable at each z in $\mathbb{C}$, and

$$f'(z) = \frac{\partial u}{\partial x}(x,y) + i\,\frac{\partial v}{\partial x}(x,y) = e^x(\cos y + i \sin y) = e^z.$$

$f(z) = e^z$ is entire.

11. A counter-example

$f(x+iy) = u(x,y) + i\,v(x,y)$

(u as in graph)   (v is zero)

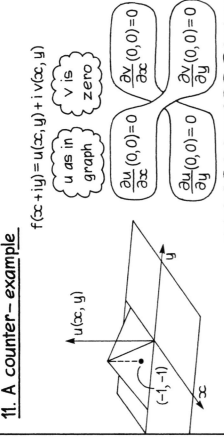

$(-1,-1)$

$\dfrac{\partial u}{\partial x}(0,0) = 0$ $\dfrac{\partial v}{\partial x}(0,0) = 0$

$\dfrac{\partial u}{\partial y}(0,0) = 0$ $\dfrac{\partial v}{\partial y}(0,0) = 0$

(Cauchy–Riemann equations hold at $(0,0)$.)

BUT

$$\lim_{n\to\infty} \frac{f(z_n) - f(0)}{z_n - 0} \begin{cases} = 0, & z_n = \frac{1}{n} \\ \neq 0, & z_n = -\frac{1}{n} - \frac{i}{n} \end{cases}$$

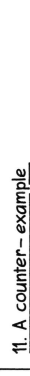

$z_n = \frac{1}{n}$

$z_n = -\frac{1}{n} - \frac{i}{n}$

12. Cauchy–Riemann Converse Theorem

($f : \mathcal{R} \longrightarrow \mathbb{C}$, $u = \mathrm{Re}\,f$, $v = \mathrm{Im}\,f$, $a + ib \in \mathcal{R}$)

If $\dfrac{\partial u}{\partial x}, \dfrac{\partial u}{\partial y}, \dfrac{\partial v}{\partial x}$ and $\dfrac{\partial v}{\partial y}$

1. exist on $\mathcal{R}$,

2. are continuous at (a,b),

3. satisfy the Cauchy–Riemann equations at (a,b),

then f is differentiable at $a + ib$ and

$$f'(a+ib) = \frac{\partial u}{\partial x}(a,b) + i\,\frac{\partial v}{\partial x}(a,b).$$

(proof in Subsection 2.2)

Problem 2.4 _____

For each function u below, calculate $\partial u/\partial x$ and $\partial u/\partial y$. Evaluate these partial derivatives at $(1, 0)$.

(a) $u(x, y) = x^3 y - y \cos y$ (b) $u(x, y) = y e^x - x y^3$

Problem 2.5 _____

Use the Cauchy–Riemann Theorems to find the derivatives of the following functions. In each case specify the domain of the derivative.

(a) $f(z) = \sin z$ (b) $f(z) = |z|^2$

2.2 Proofs

In the audio tape, we introduced two theorems: the Cauchy–Riemann Theorem, and the Cauchy–Riemann Converse Theorem. These two theorems can be used to check whether or not a given function is differentiable.

Theorem 2.1 Cauchy–Riemann Theorem

If f is differentiable at $\alpha = a + ib$, then $\dfrac{\partial u}{\partial x}, \dfrac{\partial u}{\partial y}, \dfrac{\partial v}{\partial x}, \dfrac{\partial v}{\partial y}$ exist at (a, b) and

$$\frac{\partial u}{\partial x}(a, b) = \frac{\partial v}{\partial y}(a, b) \quad \text{and} \quad \frac{\partial v}{\partial x}(a, b) = -\frac{\partial u}{\partial y}(a, b).$$

The proof of the Cauchy–Riemann Theorem is given in Frames 6 and 7.

The Cauchy–Riemann Theorem specifies equations that any differentiable complex function must satisfy. These equations are known as the **Cauchy–Riemann equations**. A function that fails to satisfy the Cauchy–Riemann equations cannot be differentiable.

Strategy C for non-differentiability

Let $f(x + iy) = u(x, y) + iv(x, y)$. If either

$$\frac{\partial u}{\partial x}(a, b) \neq \frac{\partial v}{\partial y}(a, b) \quad \text{or} \quad \frac{\partial v}{\partial x}(a, b) \neq -\frac{\partial u}{\partial y}(a, b),$$

then f is not differentiable at $a + ib$.

Strategies A and B appear in Section 1.

The Cauchy–Riemann Converse Theorem can be used to show that a given function _is_ differentiable and to find its derivative. The function not only has to satisfy the Cauchy–Riemann equations, but the partial derivatives of its real and imaginary part functions must exist and be continuous.

Theorem 2.2 Cauchy–Riemann Converse Theorem

Let $f(x + iy) = u(x, y) + iv(x, y)$ be defined on a region $\mathcal{R}$ containing $\alpha = a + ib$. If the partial derivatives $\dfrac{\partial u}{\partial x}, \dfrac{\partial u}{\partial y}, \dfrac{\partial v}{\partial x}, \dfrac{\partial v}{\partial y}$

1. exist on $\mathcal{R}$,
2. are continuous at (a, b),
3. satisfy the Cauchy–Riemann equations at (a, b),

then f is differentiable at $a + ib$ and

$$f'(a + ib) = \frac{\partial u}{\partial x}(a, b) + i \frac{\partial v}{\partial x}(a, b).$$

To prove the Cauchy–Riemann Converse Theorem we shall need two results from real analysis. The first result is known as the Mean Value Theorem.

The proof of the Cauchy–Riemann Converse Theorem may be omitted on a first reading.

Theorem 2.3 Mean Value Theorem

Let f be a real function continuous on the closed interval $[a, x]$ and differentiable on the open interval $]a, x[$. Then there is a number $c \in]a, x[$ such that

$$f(x) = f(a) + (x - a)f'(c). \qquad (*)$$

If you are not familiar with this theorem then imagine pushing the chord in Figure 2.1 parallel to itself until it becomes a tangent to the graph of f at a point $(c, f(c))$, where c lies somewhere between a and x. Clearly the slope of the original chord must be equal to the slope of the tangent, so:

$$\frac{f(x) - f(a)}{x - a} = f'(c).$$

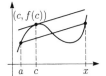

Figure 2.1

Multiplication by $x - a$ gives $(*)$. Notice that $(*)$ is also true if $x = a$.

The second result that we shall need is a Linear Approximation Theorem which asserts that if u is a real-valued function of two real variables x and y, then for (x, y) near (a, b) the value of $u(x, y)$ may be approximated by the value of the linear function t defined by

$$t(x, y) = u(a, b) + (x - a)\frac{\partial u}{\partial x}(a, b) + (y - b)\frac{\partial u}{\partial y}(a, b).$$

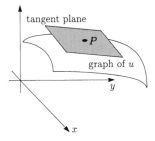

Figure 2.2

Now the graph of t is a plane passing through the point $P = (a, b, u(a, b))$ on the graph of u (Figure 2.2). Moreover, the partial x- and y-derivatives of t coincide with the partial x- and y-derivatives of u at (a, b). This means that both have the same slope in the x- and y-directions, and so you can think of the plane as the *tangent plane* to the graph of u at P.

The accuracy with which this tangent plane approximates the graph of u depends on the smoothness of the graph of u. If the graph exhibits the kind of kinks shown in Frame 11, then the approximation is not as good as for a function with continuous partial derivatives.

Theorem 2.4 Linear Approximation Theorem ($\mathbb{R}^2$ to $\mathbb{R}$)

Let u be a real-valued function of two real variables, defined on a region $\mathcal{R}$ containing (a, b). If the partial x- and y-derivatives of u exist on $\mathcal{R}$ and are continuous at (a, b), then there is an 'error function' e such that

$$u(x, y) = u(a, b) + (x - a)\frac{\partial u}{\partial x}(a, b) + (y - b)\frac{\partial u}{\partial y}(a, b) + e(x, y),$$

where $e(x, y)/\sqrt{(x - a)^2 + (y - b)^2} \to 0$ as $(x, y) \to (a, b)$.

Since $\sqrt{(x - a)^2 + (y - b)^2}$ is the distance from (a, b) to (x, y), the theorem asserts that the error function tends to zero 'faster' than this distance. It is the real analogue of Theorem 1.2.

Proof We have to show that the function e defined by

$$e(x, y) = u(x, y) - u(a, b) - (x - a)\frac{\partial u}{\partial x}(a, b) - (y - b)\frac{\partial u}{\partial y}(a, b),$$

satisfies

$$e(x, y)/\sqrt{(x - a)^2 + (y - b)^2} \to 0 \text{ as } (x, y) \to (a, b).$$

Since the partial derivatives exist on $\mathcal{R}$ they must be defined on some disc centred at (a, b). Let us begin by finding an expression for $u(x, y) - u(a, b)$ on this disc. If we apply the Mean Value Theorem to the real functions $x \longmapsto u(x, y)$ (where y is kept constant), and $y \longmapsto u(a, y)$ we obtain:

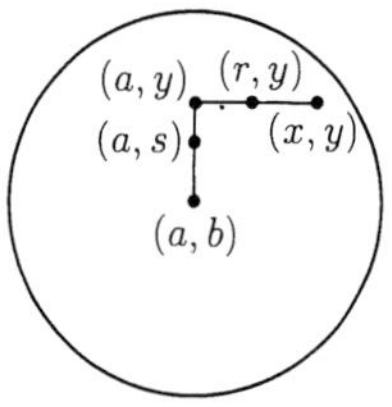

$$u(x, y) = u(a, y) + (x - a)\frac{\partial u}{\partial x}(r, y),$$

where r is between a and x, and

$$u(a, y) = u(a, b) + (y - b)\frac{\partial u}{\partial y}(a, s),$$

where s is between b and y (see Figure 2.3). Hence

$$u(x, y) - u(a, b) = (u(x, y) - u(a, y)) + (u(a, y) - u(a, b))$$

$$= (x - a)\frac{\partial u}{\partial x}(r, y) + (y - b)\frac{\partial u}{\partial y}(a, s).$$

Figure 2.3

Adding and subtracting $u(a, y)$

Substituting this expression for $u(x, y) - u(a, b)$ into the definition of e, we obtain

$$e(x, y) = (x - a)\left(\frac{\partial u}{\partial x}(r, y) - \frac{\partial u}{\partial x}(a, b)\right) + (y - b)\left(\frac{\partial u}{\partial y}(a, s) - \frac{\partial u}{\partial y}(a, b)\right).$$

Dividing by $\sqrt{(x - a)^2 + (y - b)^2}$ and noting that

$$\frac{|x - a|}{\sqrt{(x - a)^2 + (y - b)^2}} \leq 1 \quad \text{and} \quad \frac{|y - b|}{\sqrt{(x - a)^2 + (y - b)^2}} \leq 1,$$

we see that

$$\left|\frac{e(x, y)}{\sqrt{(x - a)^2 + (y - b)^2}}\right| \leq \left|\frac{\partial u}{\partial x}(r, y) - \frac{\partial u}{\partial x}(a, b)\right| + \left|\frac{\partial u}{\partial y}(a, s) - \frac{\partial u}{\partial y}(a, b)\right|.$$

This is because both $(x - a)^2$ and $(y - b)^2$ do not exceed $(x - a)^2 + (y - b)^2$.

Figure 2.3 illustrates that as (x, y) tends to (a, b), so do (a, s) and (r, y). So, by the continuity of the partial x- and y-derivatives at (a, b), the two terms on the right of the above inequality must both tend to 0 as (x, y) tends to (a, b). It follows that $e(x, y)/\sqrt{(x - a)^2 + (y - b)^2}$ tends to 0 as (x, y) tends to (a, b). ∎

We are now in a position to prove the Cauchy–Riemann Converse Theorem.

Proof of the Cauchy–Riemann Converse Theorem

We need to show that the limit of the difference quotient for f exists at α and has the value indicated in the theorem. In order to calculate the difference quotient for f at α, we find an expression for $f(z) - f(\alpha)$. Since u and v fulfil the conditions of Theorem 2.4, it follows that

$$f(z) - f(\alpha) = (u(x, y) - u(a, b)) + i(v(x, y) - v(a, b))$$

$$= \left((x - a)\frac{\partial u}{\partial x}(a, b) + (y - b)\frac{\partial u}{\partial y}(a, b) + e_u(x, y)\right)$$

$$+ i\left((x - a)\frac{\partial v}{\partial x}(a, b) + (y - b)\frac{\partial v}{\partial y}(a, b) + e_v(x, y)\right),$$

where e_u and e_v are the error functions associated with u and v, respectively.

Collecting together terms, we obtain the following expression for $f(z) - f(\alpha)$:

$$(x - a)\left(\frac{\partial u}{\partial x}(a, b) + i\frac{\partial v}{\partial x}(a, b)\right) + i(y - b)\left(\frac{\partial v}{\partial y}(a, b) - i\frac{\partial u}{\partial y}(a, b)\right)$$

$$+ e_u(x, y) + ie_v(x, y).$$

Since u and v satisfy the Cauchy–Riemann equations, both expressions in the large brackets must be equal, and so

$$f(z) - f(\alpha) = ((x - a) + i(y - b))\left(\frac{\partial u}{\partial x}(a, b) + i\frac{\partial v}{\partial x}(a, b)\right)$$

$$+ e_u(x, y) + ie_v(x, y).$$

Division by $z - \alpha = (x - a) + i(y - b)$ shows that the difference quotient is equal to

$$\frac{f(z) - f(\alpha)}{z - \alpha} = \left(\frac{\partial u}{\partial x}(a,b) + i\frac{\partial v}{\partial x}(a,b)\right) + \left(\frac{e_u(x,y) + ie_v(x,y)}{(x-a) + i(y-b)}\right).$$

The limit $f'(\alpha)$ of this difference quotient exists, and has the required value

$$\frac{\partial u}{\partial x}(a,b) + i\frac{\partial v}{\partial x}(a,b),$$

provided that we can show that the expression involving the error functions e_u and e_v tends to 0 as $z = x + iy$ tends to α. To this end, notice that $|(x - a) + i(y - b)|$ is equal to $\sqrt{(x-a)^2 + (y-b)^2}$ and so, by the Triangle Inequality,

$$\left|\frac{e_u(x,y) + ie_v(x,y)}{(x-a) + i(y-b)}\right| \leq \left|\frac{e_u(x,y)}{\sqrt{(x-a)^2 + (y-b)^2}}\right| + \left|\frac{e_v(x,y)}{\sqrt{(x-a)^2 + (y-b)^2}}\right|.$$

By Theorem 2.4, both expressions on the right tend to 0 as $x + iy$ tends to α. Consequently, the expression on the left must also tend to 0, and the theorem follows. ∎

3 THE COMPOSITION, INVERSE AND RESTRICTION RULES

After working through this section, you should be able to:

(a) use the Composition Rule, the Inverse Function Rule and the Restriction Rule to differentiate complex functions;

(b) differentiate the *principal logarithm* and *power functions*;

(c) use the table of standard derivatives.

Up to now, we have described how to differentiate the complex exponential function and rational functions. However, this still leaves a large class of functions, such as $f(z) = \exp\left(1/z^2\right)$ and $f(z) = \text{Log } z$. As in real analysis, we develop rules for differentiating composites and inverses.

3.1 The Composition Rule

Using the geometric interpretation of complex differentiation discussed in Section 1, we would expect the composite $g \circ f$ of two differentiable functions to behave in the manner illustrated in Figure 3.1. To a close approximation, f rotates and scales any small disc centred at α by the complex factor $f'(\alpha)$, producing a small disc centred at $f(\alpha)$. This is then rotated and scaled under g by a further factor $g'(f(\alpha))$, to produce a small disc centred at $g(f(\alpha))$.

The above interpretation requires that $f'(\alpha) \neq 0$ and $g'(f(\alpha)) \neq 0$.

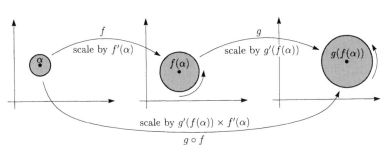

Figure 3.1

Overall, the original disc is scaled and rotated by the product of the two factors $g'(f(\alpha))$ and $f'(\alpha)$. This suggests that, as for real differentiation,

$$(g \circ f)'(\alpha) = g'(f(\alpha)) \times f'(\alpha).$$

The following theorem confirms that this is indeed the case.

Theorem 3.1 Composition Rule

Let f and g be complex functions, and let α be a limit point of the domain of $g \circ f$. If f is differentiable at α, and g is differentiable at $f(\alpha)$, then $g \circ f$ is differentiable at α, and

$$(g \circ f)'(\alpha) = g'(f(\alpha))f'(\alpha).$$

Remark The Composition Rule for differentiation is also known as the Chain Rule. We shall often use this term because, unlike 'Composition Rule', it is not used in contexts other than differentiation.

Before proving this theorem we illustrate how it is used.

Page 26

Example 3.1

Show that the function $k(z) = \exp\left(1/z^2\right)$ is analytic on its domain, and find its derivative.

Solution

The function k can be expressed as the composite $g \circ f$ of the functions

$$g(z) = \exp z \quad \text{and} \quad f(z) = 1/z^2.$$

The domain of $k = g \circ f$ is the set $A = \mathbb{C} - \{0\}$. Since this is a region, every point $z \in A$ is a limit point of A.

Now f is differentiable on A, and g is differentiable on $f(A)$. Furthermore,

$$g'(z) = \exp z \quad \text{and} \quad f'(z) = -2/z^3.$$

By the Chain Rule, $k = g \circ f$ is differentiable on A, and

$$\begin{aligned} k'(z) &= g'(f(z))f'(z) \\ &= \exp\left(1/z^2\right) \times \left(-2/z^3\right) \\ &= -2\exp\left(1/z^2\right)/z^3. \quad \blacksquare \end{aligned}$$

It is worth noting that the condition in the Composition Rule, about α being a limit point, rarely causes a problem. If the domain A of $g \circ f$ is a region, then every point of A is automatically a limit point of A.

Problem 3.1 _____

Show that each of the following functions is analytic on its domain, and find its derivative.

(a) $k(z) = (z+5)^{900}$ (b) $k(z) = \exp(z^2+4)$

(c) $k(z) = e^{\alpha z}$, where $\alpha \in \mathbb{C}$

The next example shows how part (c) of the above problem can be used to differentiate the standard trigonometric functions.

Example 3.2

Show that each of the following complex functions is analytic on its domain, and find its derivative.

(a) sin   (b) cos   (c) tan

Solution

Since the functions $z \longmapsto e^{iz}$ and $z \longmapsto e^{-iz}$ are entire, with derivatives $z \longmapsto ie^{iz}$ and $z \longmapsto -ie^{-iz}$ respectively, it follows from the Combination Rules that:

(a) $\sin z = \left(e^{iz} - e^{-iz}\right)/2i$ is entire, and

$$\sin' z = \frac{ie^{iz} - \left(-ie^{-iz}\right)}{2i} = \frac{e^{iz} + e^{-iz}}{2} = \cos z.$$

(b) $\cos z = \left(e^{iz} + e^{-iz}\right)/2i$ is entire, and

$$\cos' z = \frac{ie^{iz} + \left(-ie^{-iz}\right)}{2} = \frac{-\left(e^{iz} - e^{-iz}\right)}{2i} = -\sin z.$$

(c) $\tan z = \sin z / \cos z$ is analytic on its domain, and

$$\tan' z = \frac{\cos z \times \cos z - \sin z \times (-\sin z)}{\cos^2 z} = \frac{1}{\cos^2 z} = \sec^2 z. \quad \blacksquare$$

The domain of tan is
$$\mathbb{C} - \{(n + \tfrac{1}{2})\pi : n \in \mathbb{Z}\}.$$

The hyperbolic functions can be differentiated in a similar way.

Problem 3.2

Show that each of the following complex functions is analytic on its domain, and find its derivative.

(a) sinh   (b) cosh   (c) tanh

The Composition Rule can be extended to composites of three (or more) functions. For example, if α is a limit point of the domain of the composite $h \circ g \circ f$, and if h, g and f are differentiable at $g(f(\alpha))$, $f(\alpha)$ and α, respectively, then:

$$(h \circ g \circ f)'(\alpha) = (h \circ g)'(f(\alpha)) \times f'(\alpha) = h'(g(f(\alpha))) \times g'(f(\alpha)) \times f'(\alpha).$$

In general, to differentiate the composite of two or more functions, simply take the product of all the derivatives, keeping their inputs the same as they were prior to differentiation. With a little practice, you should be able to find the derivative of a composite function without explicitly writing down the intermediate functions.

If h, g, and f are differentiable on their domains, then they will automatically be differentiable at the points $g(f(\alpha))$, $f(\alpha)$ and α, respectively.

Example 3.3

Write down the derivative of the function $k(z) = \sin(\cosh(\tan z))$. Explain why the derivative has the same domain as k.

Solution

Since k is the composite of the functions sin, cosh and tan, we can use the Chain Rule to write down the derivative of k:

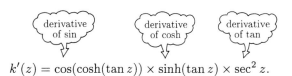

$$k'(z) = \cos(\cosh(\tan z)) \times \sinh(\tan z) \times \sec^2 z.$$

To show that k' has the same domain as k, let α be any point in the domain of k. Since the domain of k is the region $\mathbb{C} - \{(n + \tfrac{1}{2})\pi : n \in \mathbb{Z}\}$, the condition about α being a limit point is automatically satisfied. Furthermore, tan, cosh and sin are differentiable on the whole of their domains. So, in particular, they must be differentiable at α, $\tan \alpha$ and $\cosh(\tan \alpha)$, respectively. It follows that the Chain Rule can be applied throughout the domain of k, and that k' has the same domain as k. $\quad \blacksquare$

Problem 3.3

Show that each of the following functions k is analytic on its domain, and find its derivative. In (a), use the formula for differentiating a composite of three functions, given above. In (b), try to differentiate the composite functions by inspection — that is, without explicitly writing down the intermediate functions.

(a) (i) $k(z) = \left(\sin^2 z + 3\right)^2$

   (ii) $k(z) = \sin(\exp(\cos(z) - z))$

   (iii) $k(z) = \exp\left(\dfrac{1}{\cos z} + \cos z\right)$

(b) (i) $k(z) = \sin(\cosh z)$

   (ii) $k(z) = \cos\left((1 + z)^{20}\right)$

   (iii) $k(z) = \exp(\exp(\sin z))$

Proof of the Composition Rule

The idea is to write the difference quotient for $g \circ f$ in the form

$$\frac{g(f(z)) - g(f(\alpha))}{z - \alpha} = \left(\frac{g(w) - g(\beta)}{w - \beta}\right)\left(\frac{f(z) - f(\alpha)}{z - \alpha}\right), \qquad (*)$$

where $w = f(z)$ and $\beta = f(\alpha)$, and then to let $z \to \alpha$ (and hence $w \to \beta$) to obtain

$$(g \circ f)'(\alpha) = g'(\beta)f'(\alpha),$$

as required. Unfortunately there is a snag. The equation $(*)$ does not make sense if $w = \beta$ (that is, if $f(z) = f(\alpha)$) and this may conceivably happen for values of z close to α.

To avoid this problem, we introduce a function h with the same domain as g and rule

$$h(w) = \begin{cases} \dfrac{g(w) - g(\beta)}{w - \beta}, & w \neq \beta, \\ g'(\beta), & w = \beta. \end{cases}$$

Since $g'(\beta) = \lim\limits_{w \to \beta}((g(w) - g(\beta))/(w - \beta))$, this function h is continuous at β, by Theorem 3.1 of *Unit A3*. Now note that the equation

$$\frac{g(f(z)) - g(f(\alpha))}{z - \alpha} = h(f(z))\left(\frac{f(z) - f(\alpha)}{z - \alpha}\right)$$

holds for *all* z ($\neq \alpha$) in the domain of f (even if $f(z) = f(\alpha)$, since both sides then vanish). Hence, by the Product Rule for limits,

$$\lim_{z \to \alpha} \frac{g(f(z)) - g(f(\alpha))}{z - \alpha} = \lim_{z \to \alpha} h(f(z)) \lim_{z \to \alpha} \frac{f(z) - f(\alpha)}{z - \alpha}$$

$$= h(f(\alpha))f'(\alpha)$$

(since f is continuous (being differentiable) at

α and h is continuous at $\beta = f(\alpha)$)

$$= h(\beta)f'(\alpha)$$

$$= g'(\beta)f'(\alpha),$$

giving $(g \circ f)'(\alpha) = g'(f(\alpha))f'(\alpha)$, as required. ∎

3.2 The Inverse Function Rule

One striking example of a function that cannot be differentiated, using the rules that we have discussed so far, is the function Log. Recall that Log is the inverse of the function exp when restricted to the strip $\{z : -\pi < \operatorname{Im} z \le \pi\}$. In this subsection, we shall show how Log can be differentiated, using a rule that relates the derivative of a function to the derivative of its inverse.

Unit A2, Section 5

The relationship between a one-one function f and its inverse f^{-1} is illustrated in Figure 3.2. If f is differentiable at the point α and $f'(\alpha) \ne 0$, then, to a close approximation, a small disc in the domain, centred at α, is mapped to a small disc in the codomain, centred at $\beta = f(\alpha)$. In the process, the disc in the domain is rotated and scaled by the complex factor $f'(\alpha)$.

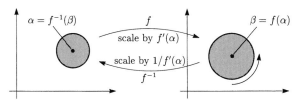

Figure 3.2

Now look at the process in reverse. The function f^{-1} takes the disc on the right, centred at β, to the disc on the left, centred at $\alpha = f^{-1}(\beta)$. As it does so, in order to undo the effect of f, f^{-1} rotates and scales the disc by the complex factor $1/f'(\alpha)$. If f^{-1} is differentiable at β, this suggest that

$$\left(f^{-1}\right)'(\beta) = 1/f'(\alpha) = 1/f'\left(f^{-1}(\beta)\right).$$

Theorem 3.2 Inverse Function Rule

Let $f : A \longrightarrow B$ be a one-one complex function, and suppose that f^{-1} is continuous at $\beta \in B$. If f has a non-zero derivative at $f^{-1}(\beta) \in A$, then f^{-1} is differentiable at β and

$$\left(f^{-1}\right)'(\beta) = \frac{1}{f'\left(f^{-1}(\beta)\right)}.$$

We give a proof of the Inverse Function Rule at the end of this subsection, but first we illustrate how it is used.

At first sight, the rule may appear to be of limited use since many complex functions are not one-one. But, as we mentioned in *Unit A2*, it is usually possible to restrict the domain of a function so as to yield a new function that *is* one-one. For example, exp is a many-one function, and yet the restriction defined by

$$f(z) = \exp z \qquad (-\pi < \operatorname{Im} z \le \pi),$$

is a one-one function whose inverse f^{-1} is the principal logarithm Log (with domain $\mathbb{C} - \{0\}$). Note that we have used an abbreviated form for the domain of f because the full version ($z \in \{z : \ldots\}$) is rather clumsy here. We shall use such abbreviated forms when convenient.

Example 3.4

Find the derivative of Log.

Solution

Let f be the restriction of exp defined by

$$f(z) = \exp z \qquad (-\pi < \operatorname{Im} z \leq \pi).$$

Then f is one-one and $f'(z) = \exp' z = \exp z \neq 0$.

At points on the negative real axis, $f^{-1} = \text{Log}$ is not differentiable because it is discontinuous. But at any other point in its domain Log is continuous. So, by Theorem 3.2, the derivative of Log is

$$\text{Log}'\, z = \frac{1}{f'\left(f^{-1}(z)\right)} = \frac{1}{\exp'(\text{Log}\, z)} = \frac{1}{\exp(\text{Log}\, z)} = \frac{1}{z},$$

where z is neither zero nor a negative real number (see Figure 3.3). ∎

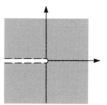

Figure 3.3 Log is analytic on the cut plane

$$\mathbb{C} - \{x \in \mathbb{R} : x \leq 0\}$$

The derivative of Log is so important that we quote the result obtained in Example 3.4 as a corollary of the Inverse Function Rule.

Corollary 1 The derivative of the principal logarithm Log is

$$\text{Log}'\, z = \frac{1}{z} \qquad (z \in \mathbb{C} - \{x \in \mathbb{R} : x \leq 0\}).$$

Problem 3.4

Find the derivative of the function $f(z) = \text{Log}(1 + iz)$ and specify its domain.

Having found the derivative of Log, we can now differentiate the principal power function $f(z) = z^\alpha$, by using the Chain Rule. Indeed, for any $\alpha \in \mathbb{C} - \mathbb{Z}$, we have

$$f(z) = z^\alpha = \exp(\alpha \,\text{Log}\, z) \qquad (z \in \mathbb{C} - \{x \in \mathbb{R} : x \leq 0\}),$$

which can be differentiated as follows:

$$\begin{aligned} f'(z) &= \exp(\alpha \,\text{Log}\, z) \times (\alpha \,\text{Log}'\, z) \\ &= \alpha \cdot z^\alpha \cdot 1/z \\ &= \alpha z^{\alpha - 1} \qquad (z \in \mathbb{C} - \{x \in \mathbb{R} : x \leq 0\}). \end{aligned}$$

We state this result as another corollary of the Inverse Function Rule.

Corollary 2 Let $\alpha \in \mathbb{C} - \mathbb{Z}$. Then the derivative of the principal power function $f(z) = z^\alpha$ is

$$f'(z) = \alpha z^{\alpha - 1} \qquad (z \in \mathbb{C} - \{x \in \mathbb{R} : x \leq 0\}).$$

Notice that this formula for differentiating *principal* powers is the same as the formula for differentiating *integer* powers given in Section 1. The only difference is the domain. Thus, for positive integer powers the domain is $\mathbb{C}$; for negative integer powers the domain is $\mathbb{C} - \{0\}$; and for general (principal) powers, the domain is the cut plane $\mathbb{C} - \{x \in \mathbb{R} : x \leq 0\}$.

Problem 3.5

Find the derivative of each of the following power functions. In each case specify the domain of the derivative.

(a) $f(z) = z^\pi$ (b) $f(z) = z^{3/2}$ (c) $f(z) = z^5$ (d) $f(z) = z^{-3}$

Proof of the Inverse Function Rule

Let $f : A \longrightarrow B$ be a one-one complex function such that f^{-1} is continuous at $\beta \in B$, and suppose that f has a non-zero derivative at $f^{-1}(\beta) \in A$. We have to show that f^{-1} is differentiable at β and that

$$\left(f^{-1}\right)'(\beta) = \frac{1}{f'\left(f^{-1}(\beta)\right)}.$$

We first check that β is a limit point of B. We do this by showing that there is a sequence in $B - \{\beta\}$ converging to β. Since f is differentiable at $\alpha = f^{-1}(\beta)$, it follows that α is a limit point of A. In other words, α is the limit of a sequence $\{z_n\}$ in $A - \{\alpha\}$. Now f is one-one and so $f(z_n) \neq f(\alpha)$, which equals β, so $\{f(z_n)\}$ is a sequence in $B - \{\beta\}$. Furthermore, f is differentiable and hence continuous at α, so $\{f(z_n)\}$ converges to β.

Next, let $\{w_n\}$ be any sequence in $B - \{\beta\}$, converging to β. Since f^{-1} is continuous at β, the sequence $\{z_n\}$, defined by $z_n = f^{-1}(w_n)$, must converge to $\alpha = f^{-1}(\beta)$. Furthermore, f is one-one, so $z_n \neq \alpha$, since $w_n \neq \beta$. Hence

$$\lim_{n \to \infty} \frac{f^{-1}(w_n) - f^{-1}(\beta)}{w_n - \beta} = \lim_{n \to \infty} \frac{z_n - \alpha}{f(z_n) - f(\alpha)} = \lim_{n \to \infty} 1 \bigg/ \frac{f(z_n) - f(\alpha)}{z_n - \alpha}.$$

Since f is differentiable at α, and since $f'(\alpha) = f'(f^{-1}(\beta))$ is assumed to be non-zero, it follows from the Quotient Rule for sequences that the last limit exists, and is equal to $\dfrac{1}{f'\left(f^{-1}(\beta)\right)}$, as required. ∎

3.3 The Restriction Rule

When applying the Inverse Function Rule to the exponential function in the previous subsection, we ignored one technicality. We assumed that because the exponential function is differentiable, its restriction to the set

$$\{z : -\pi < \operatorname{Im} z \leq \pi\}$$

is also differentiable. This is not quite the same as saying that exp is differentiable on the set $\{z : -\pi < \operatorname{Im} z \leq \pi\}$. It is saying that a *new* function formed by restricting exp to $\{z : -\pi < \operatorname{Im} z \leq \pi\}$ is differentiable on its own domain.

The justification for assuming that the restriction of exp to $\{z : -\pi < \operatorname{Im} z \leq \pi\}$ is differentiable is provided by the following theorem.

Theorem 3.3 Restriction Rule

Let f, g be complex functions with domains A, B respectively and let $A \subseteq B$. If $\alpha \in A$ is a limit point of A and

1. $f(z) = g(z)$, for $z \in A$,
2. g is differentiable at α,

then f is differentiable at α, and $f'(\alpha) = g'(\alpha)$.

Proof Let $\{z_n\}$ be any sequence in $A - \{\alpha\}$ converging to α. We need to show that

$$\lim_{n \to \infty} \frac{f(z_n) - f(\alpha)}{z_n - \alpha} = g'(\alpha).$$

Since $A \subseteq B$, $\{z_n\}$ is a sequence in $B - \{\alpha\}$ converging to α. It follows from the second condition that

$$\lim_{n \to \infty} \frac{g(z_n) - g(\alpha)}{z_n - \alpha} = g'(\alpha).$$

By the first condition, $f(z_n) = g(z_n)$ and $f(\alpha) = g(\alpha)$, and so the result follows. ∎

In essence the Restriction Rule tells us that we need not worry too much about the domain of a function that we are trying to differentiate. It tells us that, provided we avoid leaving 'isolated points', then we can cut away unwanted parts of the domain of a differentiable function without affecting its differentiability at the remaining points.

The Restriction Rule explains why many real functions have the same derivative as their complex counterparts. For example, the derivative of the real sine function is the real cosine function; this may be explained by restricting the complex sine function to the real axis and applying the Restriction Rule. Similarly, the derivative of the real logarithm function may be obtained from the derivative of Log by restricting Log to the positive real axis $]0, \infty[$ and applying the Restriction Rule.

3.4 Standard functions

To end this section, we collect together a list of the functions that have been differentiated in this unit, together with their derivatives.

f	Rule of f'	Domain of f'
$f(z) = \alpha, \quad \alpha \in \mathbb{C}$	$f'(z) = 0$	$\mathbb{C}$
$f(z) = z^k, \quad k \in \mathbb{Z}, k > 0$	$f'(z) = kz^{k-1}$	$\mathbb{C}$
$f(z) = z^k, \quad k \in \mathbb{Z}, k < 0$	$f'(z) = kz^{k-1}$	$\mathbb{C} - \{0\}$
$f(z) = z^\alpha, \quad \alpha \in \mathbb{C} - \mathbb{Z}$	$f'(z) = \alpha z^{\alpha-1}$	$\mathbb{C} - \{x \in \mathbb{R} : x \le 0\}$
$f(z) = \exp z$	$f'(z) = \exp z$	$\mathbb{C}$
$f(z) = \operatorname{Log} z$	$f'(z) = 1/z$	$\mathbb{C} - \{x \in \mathbb{R} : x \le 0\}$
$f(z) = \sin z$	$f'(z) = \cos z$	$\mathbb{C}$
$f(z) = \cos z$	$f'(z) = -\sin z$	$\mathbb{C}$
$f(z) = \tan z$	$f'(z) = \sec^2 z$	$\mathbb{C} - \left\{\left(n + \frac{1}{2}\right)\pi : n \in \mathbb{Z}\right\}$
$f(z) = \sinh z$	$f'(z) = \cosh z$	$\mathbb{C}$
$f(z) = \cosh z$	$f'(z) = \sinh z$	$\mathbb{C}$
$f(z) = \tanh z$	$f'(z) = \operatorname{sech}^2 z$	$\mathbb{C} - \left\{\left(n + \frac{1}{2}\right)\pi i : n \in \mathbb{Z}\right\}$

The formula for differentiating non-zero powers always has the same form, but the domain of the derivative changes. For natural powers the domain is $\mathbb{C}$; for negative integer powers, 0 is excluded; and for general (principal) powers, the negative reals and 0 are excluded.

By applying the Combination, Composition, and Inverse Rules to the above list of 'standard' functions, it is possible to differentiate most of the functions that you are likely to encounter in this course. If necessary, the Restriction Rule can then be applied to obtain a function with the required domain.

Example 3.5

Find the derivative of each of the following functions f.

(a) $f(z) = 5 + 2\sin z \cosh z$
(b) $f(z) = \dfrac{e^z}{z + \sinh z - 2\cosh z}$

(c) $f(z) = z \exp\left(2z^2 + z\right)$

Solution

(a) By the Combination Rules:
$$f'(z) = 2(\cos z \cosh z + \sin z \sinh z).$$

(b) By the Combination Rules:
$$f'(z) = \frac{(z + \sinh z - 2\cosh z)e^z - e^z(1 + \cosh z - 2\sinh z)}{(z + \sinh z - 2\cosh z)^2}$$
$$= \frac{(-1 + z + 3\sinh z - 3\cosh z)e^z}{(z + \sinh z - 2\cosh z)^2}.$$

(c) By the Chain Rule, Product Rule, and the rule for differentiating polynomials:

$$f'(z) = 1 \times \exp\left(2z^2 + z\right) + z\left(\exp\left(2z^2 + z\right)\right)(4z + 1)$$
$$= \left(1 + z + 4z^2\right)\exp\left(2z^2 + z\right). \quad \blacksquare$$

For further practice in using the rules of differentiation, try the following problem.

Problem 3.6

Find the derivative of each of the following functions f. In each case specify the domain of the derivative.

(a) $f(z) = 3 + e^z \operatorname{Log} z$ (b) $f(z) = (z + \sin z)^{20}$

(c) $f(z) = \cos^2(z + \cosh z)$ (d) $f(z) = \dfrac{\operatorname{Log} z}{z}$

4 SMOOTH PATHS

After working through this section, you should be able to:

(a) differentiate a parametrization;

(b) decide whether a path is *smooth*;

(c) interpret the derivative of an analytic function as a rotation and a scaling of tangent vectors;

(d) find the *angle* between two smooth paths at a point of intersection;

(e) understand the manner in which analytic functions preserve angle.

4.1 Derivatives of parametrizations

Recall that in *Unit A2* we defined a *path* to be a subset Γ of $\mathbb{C}$ which is the image of an associated continuous function $\gamma : I \longrightarrow \mathbb{C}$, where I is a real interval. The function γ is called a *parametrization*. (See Figure 4.1.)

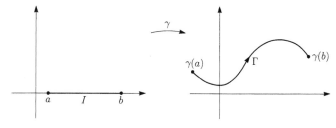

We have drawn the interval I as a subset of the complex plane to emphasize that γ is a complex function to which the theory of complex differentiation may be applied.

Figure 4.1 A path $\Gamma : \gamma(t) \quad (t \in I)$

Problem 4.1

Sketch the paths with the following parametrizations using an arrow to indicate the direction of the path.

(a) $\gamma(t) = \exp(it) \quad (t \in [0, 2\pi])$

(b) $\gamma(t) = \sin t + i|t| \quad (t \in [-\pi/2, \pi/2])$

(c) $\gamma(t) = t^2 + it^3 \quad (t \in [-1, 1])$

In this section we apply the theory of differentiation to parametrizations. Geometrically, if the derivative of a parametrization γ exists at c (and is non-zero), then it may be interpreted as a tangent vector to the path Γ at $\gamma(c)$. This is because the difference quotient

$$\frac{\gamma(t) - \gamma(c)}{t - c}$$

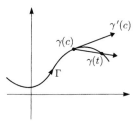

Figure 4.2

may be represented in the complex plane by a vector lying along the line through $\gamma(c)$ and $\gamma(t)$ (see Figure 4.2). In fact, it is the vector obtained by scaling the vector from $\gamma(c)$ to $\gamma(t)$ by the real factor $1/(t-c)$. Now, as t approaches c, the line through $\gamma(c)$ and $\gamma(t)$ becomes tangential to the path; so, in the limit, $\gamma'(c)$ may be represented by a tangent vector to the path at $\gamma(c)$.

> Let Γ be a path with parametrization $\gamma : I \to \mathbb{C}$, and suppose that $c \in I$. If γ is differentiable at c and if $\gamma'(c) \neq 0$, then $\gamma'(c)$ may be interpreted geometrically as a *tangent vector* to the path Γ at the point $\gamma(c)$.

It is often useful to think of the tangent vector which represents $\gamma'(c)$ as the velocity vector of a particle moving along the path. If $\gamma(t)$ represents the position of the particle on the path Γ at time t then $\gamma(t) - \gamma(c)$ is the net displacement of the particle that occurs between times c and t. During this time, the velocity of the particle is approximately equal to the difference quotient

$$\frac{\gamma(t) - \gamma(c)}{t - c}.$$

The limit $\gamma'(c)$ as t tends to c is, therefore, the *velocity* of the particle at time c. With this interpretation, the direction of the tangent vector associated with $\gamma'(c)$ indicates the direction in which the particle is moving, and the length of the vector $|\gamma'(c)|$ indicates its speed.

Next we describe how to find the derivative of a parametrization $\gamma : I \longrightarrow \mathbb{C}$ (when this derivative exists). In many cases, the most convenient method is to notice that the parametrization γ is the restriction to I of a complex function whose domain is a region which contains I. For example, the parametrization

$$\gamma(t) = (1 + it)^3 \qquad (t \in [0,2])$$

is the restriction to $I = [0,2]$ of the function

$$f(z) = (1 + iz)^3,$$

whose domain is $\mathbb{C}$. Since

$$f'(z) = 3i(1 + iz)^2,$$

it follows by the Restriction Rule that

$$\gamma'(t) = 3i(1 + it)^2 \qquad (t \in [0,2]).$$

In practice, in such cases, we can treat t as if it were the complex variable z and invoke the Restriction Rule. (There is no need to set up the function f; we just 'differentiate $\gamma(t)$ with respect to t'.)

See Exercise 4.1(d) for an example for which this approach does not work.

Problem 4.2

Find the derivative of each of the following parametrizations. In each case
evaluate $\gamma'(0)$ and illustrate your answer on a sketch.

(a) $\gamma(t) = t + i(3 - t)$ $(t \in [-1, 2])$

(b) $\gamma(t) = \cos t + 2i \sin t$ $(t \in [0, 2\pi])$

(c) $\gamma(t) = t^2 + 2it$ $(t \in \mathbb{R})$

(d) $\gamma(t) = 2 \cosh t + 3i \sinh t$ $(t \in \mathbb{R})$

(e) $\gamma(t) = e^{it}$ $(t \in [0, 2\pi])$

The next result gives a useful method of spotting points at which a
parametrization is *not* differentiable.

Theorem 4.1 Let ϕ and ψ be real functions, both with domain some
interval I. Then the parametrization

$$\gamma(t) = \phi(t) + i\,\psi(t) \qquad (t \in I)$$

is differentiable at a point $c \in I$ if and only if both ϕ and ψ are
differentiable at c. If ϕ and ψ are differentiable at c, then

$$\gamma'(c) = \phi'(c) + i\,\psi'(c).$$

Warning! This theorem does not
apply to functions with domains
that are not contained in $\mathbb{R}$. For
example, it is not possible to use

$$z = \operatorname{Re} z + i \operatorname{Im} z$$

to deduce that Re and Im are
differentiable. They are not!

Proof If the real functions ϕ and ψ are both differentiable at c, then, by the
Sum and Multiple Rules for differentiation, γ is also differentiable at c and

$$\gamma'(c) = \phi'(c) + i\psi'(c).$$

On the other hand, if γ is differentiable at c, then

$$
\begin{aligned}
\phi'(c) &= \lim_{t \to c} \frac{\phi(t) - \phi(c)}{t - c} \\
&= \lim_{t \to c} \frac{\operatorname{Re}(\gamma(t)) - \operatorname{Re}(\gamma(c))}{t - c} \\
&= \lim_{t \to c} \operatorname{Re}\left(\frac{\gamma(t) - \gamma(c)}{t - c} \right) \\
&= \operatorname{Re}\left(\lim_{t \to c} \frac{\gamma(t) - \gamma(c)}{t - c} \right) \\
&= \operatorname{Re}(\gamma'(c)).
\end{aligned}
$$

Remember that if $\{z_n\}$ is
convergent, then

$$\lim_{n \to \infty} \operatorname{Re} z_n = \operatorname{Re}\left(\lim_{n \to \infty} z_n \right).$$

Similarly, $\psi'(c) = \operatorname{Im}(\gamma'(c))$. Thus ϕ and ψ are differentiable at c, as
required. ∎

Theorem 4.1 states that the differentiability of γ is *equivalent* to the
differentiability of its real and imaginary part functions. It follows that a
parametrization like

$$\gamma(t) = t + i|t| \qquad (t \in \mathbb{R})$$

is not differentiable at 0, since the real modulus function is not differentiable at
0. However, γ is differentiable on $\mathbb{R} - \{0\}$, since its real and imaginary part
functions are both differentiable there.

Problem 4.3

At which points does the parametrization

$$\gamma(t) = t + i\sqrt{t} \qquad (t \in [0, \infty[)$$

fail to have a derivative?

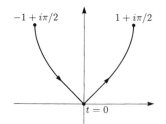

Looking at the path with parametrization

$$\gamma(t) = \sin t + i|t| \qquad (t \in [-\pi/2, \pi/2])$$

in Figure 4.3, you can see that the kink in the path at $t = 0$ coincides with the point at which γ fails to be differentiable. It is sometimes convenient to avoid such kinks by confining our attention to paths with a parametrization whose derivative exists and varies continuously along the path. Actually, we need slightly more than this because kinks can also occur when the derivative of a parametrization is zero. For example, Figure 4.4 shows the path with the parametrization

Figure 4.3

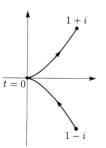

$$\gamma(t) = t^2 + it^3 \qquad (t \in [-1, 1]).$$

Although this parametrization is differentiable on its domain, its derivative is zero at the kink. In terms of the particle analogy, a zero derivative gives rise to a point on the path where the particle stops instantaneously. At this point, the particle is able to change direction abruptly, but without upsetting the continuity of the velocity.

Figure 4.4

Another example of where a zero derivative can lead to difficulties is shown in Figure 4.5. This is the path with the parametrization

$$\gamma(t) = (t^3 - 3t) + i \qquad (t \in \mathbb{R}).$$

The derivative of this parametrization is zero when t is equal to -1 or 1, so the particle is able to 'reverse' at these points and retrace points already covered.

Figure 4.5

When we wish to avoid the kinds of behaviour exhibited in Figures 4.3–4.5 we confine our attention to paths that are *smooth* in the following sense.

Definition A parametrization $\gamma : I \to \mathbb{C}$ is **smooth** if

(a) γ is differentiable on I;

(b) γ' is continuous on I;

(c) γ' is non-zero on I.

A path is **smooth** if its parametrization is smooth.

Problem 4.4

Decide which of the following parametrizations are smooth.

(a) $\gamma(t) = t + i(1 - \cos t) \qquad (t \in [0, 2\pi])$

(b) $\gamma(t) = t^2 - 2t + i\pi \qquad (t \in [0, 2])$

(c) $\gamma(t) = \sqrt{t} + it \qquad (t \in [0, 2])$

In the next unit we shall define *integration along a smooth path*. Here we use smooth paths to pursue the geometric interpretation of derivatives that we began in Section 1.

4.2 A geometric interpretation of derivatives (revisited)

In Section 1, we interpreted the derivative of an analytic function by saying that, to a close approximation, a small disc centred at α is mapped to a small disc centred at $f(\alpha)$. In the process, the disc is rotated through the angle $\operatorname{Arg} f'(\alpha)$, and scaled by the factor $|f'(\alpha)|$ (see Figure 4.6).

This interpretation requires that $f'(\alpha) \neq 0$.

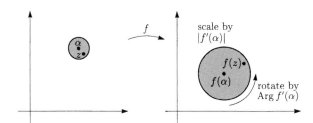

Figure 4.6   The approximate image of a small disc under an analytic function

This interpretation of $f'(\alpha)$ as a rotation and a scaling is all very well, but it is only an approximation. Fortunately, we can make the interpretation precise by examining the effect that f has on the tangent vectors to smooth paths through α.

Let f be a function which is analytic on a region $\mathcal{R}$, and let $\gamma : I \longrightarrow \mathbb{C}$ be the parametrization of a smooth path Γ contained in $\mathcal{R}$. Then $f \circ \gamma : I \longrightarrow \mathbb{C}$ is the parametrization of the image path $f(\Gamma)$ (see Figure 4.7).

Remember that $f \circ \gamma$ is the composite of two continuous functions, and is therefore continuous.

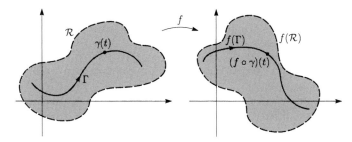

Figure 4.7   The image of a path is a path

Now consider a point $\alpha = \gamma(c)$ on the path Γ. This is mapped by f to the point $f(\alpha) = (f \circ \gamma)(c)$ on the path $f(\Gamma)$. Since the path Γ is smooth, a tangent vector to Γ at α is given by the derivative $\gamma'(c)$. Also, if $f'(\alpha) \neq 0$, then a tangent vector to $f(\Gamma)$ at $f(\alpha)$ is given by

$$(f \circ \gamma)'(c) = f'(\gamma(c))\gamma'(c) = f'(\alpha)\gamma'(c), \qquad \text{(Chain Rule)},$$

as shown in Figure 4.8.

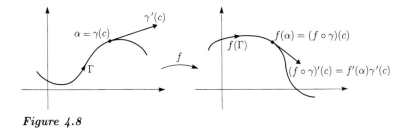

Figure 4.8

We have thus shown that the two tangent vectors are related by the complex scale factor $f'(\alpha)$, in the following way.

> Let f be a function that is analytic on a region $\mathcal{R}$, and suppose that $f'(\alpha) \neq 0$ for some $\alpha \in \mathcal{R}$. If Γ is a smooth path with parametrization γ in $\mathcal{R}$ passing through α, then the tangent vector to the image path $f(\Gamma)$ at $f(\alpha)$ may be obtained from the tangent vector to Γ at α by a rotation through the angle $\operatorname{Arg} f'(\alpha)$ and a scaling by the factor $|f'(\alpha)|$.

If $f'(\alpha) = 0$, then $f(\Gamma)$ is not smooth.

As usual, the rotation is anticlockwise if $\operatorname{Arg} f'(\alpha)$ is positive, and clockwise if it is negative.

This is the geometric interpretation of derivative that we have been seeking. It is no longer an approximate result about the effect that f has on small discs, but a precise statement about the effect that f has on tangent vectors to paths. It is summarized in Figure 4.9.

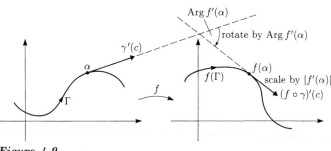

Figure 4.9

4.3 Conformal functions

There is an important corollary to the above fact about tangents. If $\Gamma_1 : \gamma_1(t)$ $(t \in I_1)$ and $\Gamma_2 : \gamma_2(t)$ $(t \in I_2)$ are two smooth paths that intersect at the point $\alpha = \gamma_1(t_1) = \gamma_2(t_2)$, say, then the angle θ between their tangents at α serves as a measure of the angle at which the paths themselves intersect (see Figure 4.10). Since $\gamma_1'(t_1)$ and $\gamma_2'(t_2)$ can be interpreted as being tangent vectors to Γ_1 and Γ_2 at α and since

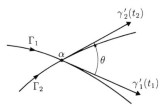

$$\gamma_2'(t_2) = \left(\frac{\gamma_2'(t_2)}{\gamma_1'(t_1)} \right) \gamma_1'(t_1),$$

the **angle θ from Γ_1 to Γ_2** is given by

$$\theta = \operatorname{Arg} \left(\frac{\gamma_2'(t_2)}{\gamma_1'(t_1)} \right). \tag{4.1}$$

Figure 4.10

Note that this definition specifies the size and orientation of one of the angles between Γ_1 and Γ_2 — that from Γ_1 to Γ_2 in the interval $]-\pi, \pi]$.

Example 4.1

Let Γ_1 and Γ_2 be the paths with parametrizations

$$\gamma_1(t) = e^t + i(1 + 3t) \qquad (t \in [-\tfrac{1}{2}, \tfrac{1}{2}]),$$
$$\gamma_2(t) = (t + 2) + it^2 \qquad (t \in [-\tfrac{3}{2}, \tfrac{1}{2}]),$$

respectively. Show that the two paths meet at the point $1 + i$, and find the angle from Γ_1 to Γ_2 at this point of intersection.

Solution

The paths Γ_1 and Γ_2 meet at $1 + i$ since

$$\gamma_1(0) = \gamma_2(-1) = 1 + i.$$

Now

$$\gamma_1'(t) = e^t + 3i \quad \text{and} \quad \gamma_2'(t) = 1 + 2ti,$$

so

$$\gamma_1'(0) = 1 + 3i \quad \text{and} \quad \gamma_2'(-1) = 1 - 2i.$$

Hence, from Equation (4.1), the angle from Γ_1 to Γ_2 at $1 + i$ is

$$
\begin{aligned}
\operatorname{Arg}\left(\frac{\gamma_2'(-1)}{\gamma_1'(0)}\right) &= \operatorname{Arg}\left(\frac{1 - 2i}{1 + 3i}\right) \\
&= \operatorname{Arg}\left(\tfrac{1}{10}(1 - 2i)(\overline{1 + 3i})\right) \\
&= \operatorname{Arg}((1 - 2i)(1 - 3i)) \\
&= \operatorname{Arg}(-5 - 5i) \\
&= -3\pi/4.
\end{aligned}
$$

So the angle from Γ_1 to Γ_2 at $1 + i$ is $3\pi/4$ clockwise (Figure 4.11). ∎

Notice that the parameters for two intersecting paths are not necessarily equal at the point of intersection.

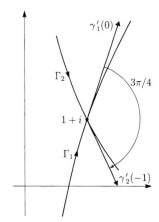

Figure 4.11

Now let us consider the effect of an analytic function f on the angle between two smooth paths Γ_1 and Γ_2 that meet at a point α. Assuming that $f'(\alpha) \neq 0$, we see that the tangents to Γ_1 and Γ_2 at α may be brought into alignment with the tangents to $f(\Gamma_1)$ and $f(\Gamma_2)$ at $f(\alpha)$ by a rotation through $\operatorname{Arg} f'(\alpha)$. Since the size and orientation of the angle between the tangents is unchanged by the rotation, the angle between the image paths $f(\Gamma_1)$ and $f(\Gamma_2)$ at $f(\alpha)$ must have the same size and orientation as the angle between the paths Γ_1 and Γ_2 at α (Figure 4.12).

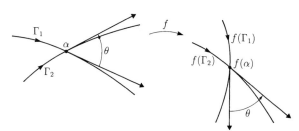

Figure 4.12

> **Definition** A function is **conformal at** α if it leaves unchanged the size and orientation of the angle between any two smooth paths through α. A function is **conformal on a set S** if it is conformal at every point of S. A function is **conformal** if it is conformal on its domain.

We sometimes abbreviate this definition by saying that conformal functions are 'angle-preserving'. Also, it is common to call functions which are conformal on their domains **conformal mappings**.

Having introduced the notion of conformal functions, we may now summarize the above discussion as follows.

> **Theorem 4.2** Let f be a function which is analytic at α, with $f'(\alpha) \neq 0$. Then f is conformal at α.

Problem 4.5

Give an example of two smooth paths through 0 such that the angle between them at 0 is not preserved under the function $f(z) = z^2$. Why does this not contradict Theorem 4.2?

A striking illustration of Theorem 4.2 occurs when Cartesian and polar grids are used to investigate the behaviour of complex functions. Several functions were investigated in this way in Section 3 of *Unit A2*. The results obtained for the functions $f(z) = z^2$ and $f(z) = 1/z$ are reproduced in Figures 4.13 and 4.14.

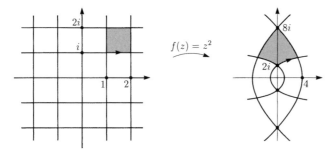

Figure 4.13   The image of a Cartesian grid under $f(z) = z^2$

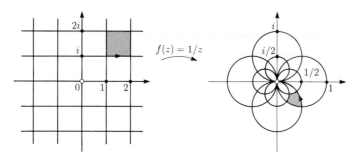

Figure 4.14   The image of a Cartesian grid under $f(z) = 1/z$

In both cases, the image of the Cartesian grid consists of paths that intersect at right angles (except at 0). Theorem 4.2 shows that this remarkable property holds for all analytic functions, provided that the derivative of the function is non-zero on the region under consideration.

Problem 4.6

What can you say about the image of a polar grid under an analytic function?

The answer to Problem 4.6 may be generalized with the help of the following definition.

Definition   Smooth paths that meet at right angles are said to be **orthogonal**. A grid made up of orthogonal smooth paths is called an **orthogonal grid**.

Theorem 4.2 shows that an analytic function f maps an orthogonal grid, over any region where f' is non-zero, to an orthogonal grid.

We shall return to the conformal properties of analytic functions later in the course.

EXERCISES

Section 1

Exercise 1.1 Use the definition of derivative to find the derivative of the function
$$f(z) = 2z^2 + 5.$$

Exercise 1.2 Prove the Quotient Rule for differentiation.

Exercise 1.3 Find the derivative of each of the following functions f. In each case, specify the domain of f'.

(a) $f(z) = \dfrac{z^2 + 2z + 1}{3z + 1}$
(b) $f(z) = \dfrac{z^3 + 1}{z^2 - z - 6}$

(c) $f(z) = \dfrac{1}{z^2 + 2z + 2}$
(d) $f(z) = z^2 + 5z - 2 + \dfrac{1}{z} + \dfrac{1}{z^2}$

Exercise 1.4 Show that there are no points of the negative real axis at which the function $f(z) = \operatorname{Arg} z$ is differentiable.

Exercise 1.5 For each of the functions f below, use Strategy B to show that there are no points of $\mathbb{C}$ at which f is differentiable.

(a) $f(z) = \operatorname{Im} z$
(b) $f(z) = 2\operatorname{Re} z + i \operatorname{Im} z$

Exercise 1.6 Describe the approximate geometric effect of the function
$$f(z) = \frac{z^3 + 8}{z - 6}$$
on a small disc centred at the point 2.

Section 2

Exercise 2.1 For each of the functions $u : \mathbb{R}^2 \longrightarrow \mathbb{R}$ below, calculate the partial derivatives $\dfrac{\partial u}{\partial x}(x, y)$ and $\dfrac{\partial u}{\partial y}(x, y)$.

(a) $u(x, y) = 3x + xy + 2x^2 y^2$
(b) $u(x, y) = x \cos y + \exp(xy)$
(c) $u(x, y) = (x + y)^3$

Exercise 2.2 Find the slope of the graph of $u(x, y) = x^2 + 2xy$ at the point $(1, 2)$ in the x-direction and in the y-direction.

Exercise 2.3 Use the Cauchy–Riemann equations to show that there is no point of $\mathbb{C}$ at which the function
$$f(x + iy) = e^x(\sin y + i \cos y)$$
is differentiable.

Exercise 2.4 Use the Cauchy–Riemann equations to show that the function $f(x + iy) = (x^2 + x - y^2) + i(2xy + y)$ is entire, and find its derivative.

Exercise 2.5 Use the Cauchy–Riemann equations to find all the points at which the following functions are differentiable, and calculate their derivatives.

(a) $f(x + iy) = (x^2 + y^2) + i(x^2 - y^2)$
(b) $f(x + iy) = xy$

Section 3

Exercise 3.1 Find the derivatives of the following functions.

(a) $\operatorname{sech} z = \dfrac{1}{\cosh z}$ (b) $\operatorname{cosech} z = \dfrac{1}{\sinh z}$ (c) $\coth z = \dfrac{\cosh z}{\sinh z}$

Exercise 3.2 Use the rules of differentiation to find the derivative of the function

$$f(z) = \operatorname{Log}(z+1) + \exp(z^2).$$

Specify the domain of f'.

Exercise 3.3 Write down (without justification) the rules of the derivatives of the following functions.

(a) $f(z) = \sin(\cos z - z)$ (b) $f(z) = z \exp(z^2 + i) + \cos z$

(c) $f(z) = \dfrac{\operatorname{Log} z}{\exp(z+1)}$ (d) $f(z) = \cos(3\sin(i + \tan z))$

Section 4

Exercise 4.1 Find the derivatives of each of the following parametrizations.

(a) $\gamma(t) = \exp(t^2 + it)$ $(t \in [-1, 1])$
(b) $\gamma(t) = t^2 + i\cos t$ $(t \in [0, 2])$
(c) $\gamma(t) = 5\cos t + 7i\sin t$ $(t \in [-\pi, \pi])$
(d) $\gamma(t) = |t| + (t^4 + t)i$ $(t \in [-1, 1])$

Exercise 4.2 Which of the parametrizations in Exercise 4.1 are smooth?

Exercise 4.3

(a) Let Γ_1 and Γ_2 be the paths with parametrizations

$$\gamma_1(t) = 2\sin t + i(t+1) \qquad (t \in [0, 2]),$$
$$\gamma_2(t) = (1 - t) + it^2 \qquad (t \in [-1, 2]),$$

respectively. Show that the two paths meet at the point i, and find the angle from Γ_1 to Γ_2 at this point of intersection.

(b) Now let $f(z) = \sin^2 z$. What is the angle from $f(\Gamma_1)$ to $f(\Gamma_2)$ at $f(i)$?

SOLUTIONS TO THE PROBLEMS

Section 1

1.1 (a) $f(z) = 1$ is defined on the whole of $\mathbb{C}$, so let $\alpha \in \mathbb{C}$. Then
$$f'(\alpha) = \lim_{z \to \alpha} \frac{f(z) - f(\alpha)}{z - \alpha} = \lim_{z \to \alpha} \frac{1 - 1}{z - \alpha} = \lim_{z \to \alpha} \frac{0}{z - \alpha} = 0.$$
Since α is an arbitrary complex number, f is differentiable on the whole of $\mathbb{C}$, and its derivative is the zero function
$$f'(z) = 0 \quad (z \in \mathbb{C}).$$

(b) $f(z) = z$ is defined on the whole of $\mathbb{C}$, so let $\alpha \in \mathbb{C}$. Then
$$f'(\alpha) = \lim_{z \to \alpha} \frac{f(z) - f(\alpha)}{z - \alpha} = \lim_{z \to \alpha} \frac{z - \alpha}{z - \alpha} = \lim_{z \to \alpha} 1 = 1.$$

Since α is an arbitrary complex number, f is differentiable on the whole of $\mathbb{C}$, and its derivative is the constant function
$$f'(z) = 1 \quad (z \in \mathbb{C}).$$

1.2 The domain of $f(z) = 1/z$ is the region $\mathbb{C} - \{0\}$. Since $f'(\alpha)$ cannot exist unless f is defined at α, we confine our attention to $\alpha \neq 0$. Then
$$f'(\alpha) = \lim_{z \to \alpha} \frac{f(z) - f(\alpha)}{z - \alpha}$$
$$= \lim_{z \to \alpha} \frac{(1/z) - (1/\alpha)}{z - \alpha}$$
$$= \lim_{z \to \alpha} \frac{\alpha - z}{z\alpha(z - \alpha)}$$
$$= \lim_{z \to \alpha} \frac{-1}{z\alpha}.$$
By the Quotient and Multiple Rules for limits, the final limit is equal to $-1/\alpha^2$. Since α is an arbitrary non-zero complex number, the derivative of f is
$$f'(z) = \frac{-1}{z^2} \quad (z \neq 0).$$

The function f is not entire since its domain is not $\mathbb{C}$.

1.3 (a) True

(b) False (The set must be a region.)

1.4 (a) Let $F = f + g$. Then
$$\lim_{z \to \alpha} \frac{F(z) - F(\alpha)}{z - \alpha} = \lim_{z \to \alpha} \frac{(f(z) + g(z)) - (f(\alpha) + g(\alpha))}{z - \alpha}$$
$$= \lim_{z \to \alpha} \frac{(f(z) - f(\alpha)) + (g(z) - g(\alpha))}{z - \alpha}$$
$$= \lim_{z \to \alpha} \frac{f(z) - f(\alpha)}{z - \alpha} + \lim_{z \to \alpha} \frac{g(z) - g(\alpha)}{z - \alpha}$$
$$= f'(\alpha) + g'(\alpha).$$

(b) Let $F = \lambda f$, for $\lambda \in \mathbb{C}$. Then
$$\lim_{z \to \alpha} \frac{F(z) - F(\alpha)}{z - \alpha} = \lim_{z \to \alpha} \frac{\lambda f(z) - \lambda f(\alpha)}{z - \alpha}$$
$$= \lambda \lim_{z \to \alpha} \frac{f(z) - f(\alpha)}{z - \alpha}$$
$$= \lambda f'(\alpha).$$

1.5 (a) By Corollary 2, we have
$$f'(z) = 4z^3 + 9z^2 - 2z + 4 \quad (z \in \mathbb{C}).$$

(b) By the Quotient Rule, we have
$$f'(z) = \frac{(z^2 + z + 1)(2z - 4) - (z^2 - 4z + 2)(2z + 1)}{(z^2 + z + 1)^2}$$
$$= \frac{5z^2 - 2z - 6}{(z^2 + z + 1)^2}$$
$$(z \in \mathbb{C} - \{-\tfrac{1}{2}(1 + \sqrt{3}i), -\tfrac{1}{2}(1 - \sqrt{3}i)\}).$$

1.6 The function Arg is discontinuous at each point of the negative real axis (see Frame 17, *Unit A3*). It follows that Log is discontinuous at each point of the negative real axis, and hence that there are no points on it at which Log is differentiable.

1.7 Let $z_n = \alpha \exp(i/n)$. Then z_n tends to α along the circumference of the circle, and
$$\lim_{n \to \infty} \frac{|z_n| - |\alpha|}{z_n - \alpha} = \lim_{n \to \infty} \frac{|\alpha| - |\alpha|}{z_n - \alpha} = 0.$$
Now let $z'_n = \alpha(1 + 1/n)$. Then z'_n tends to α along the radius of the circle, and
$$\lim_{n \to \infty} \frac{|z'_n| - |\alpha|}{z'_n - \alpha} = \lim_{n \to \infty} \frac{|\alpha|(1 + 1/n) - |\alpha|}{\alpha(1 + 1/n) - \alpha} = \frac{|\alpha|}{\alpha}.$$
Since $|\alpha|/\alpha \neq 0$ for $\alpha \neq 0$, these two limits do not agree. It follows that $f(z) = |z|$ is not differentiable at $\alpha \neq 0$.

1.8 Let α be an arbitrary complex number. Directions of paths parallel to the imaginary axis through α are reversed by f, while directions of paths parallel to the real axis are not. This suggests looking at the sequences $z_n = \alpha + 1/n$ and $z'_n = \alpha + i/n$.

First let $z_n = \alpha + 1/n$; then
$$\lim_{n \to \infty} \frac{\overline{z_n} - \overline{\alpha}}{z_n - \alpha} = \lim_{n \to \infty} \frac{\overline{(\alpha + 1/n)} - \overline{\alpha}}{(\alpha + 1/n) - \alpha} = \lim_{n \to \infty} \frac{1/n}{1/n} = 1.$$
Now let $z'_n = \alpha + i/n$; then
$$\lim_{n \to \infty} \frac{\overline{z'_n} - \overline{\alpha}}{z'_n - \alpha} = \lim_{n \to \infty} \frac{\overline{(\alpha + i/n)} - \overline{\alpha}}{(\alpha + i/n) - \alpha} = \lim_{n \to \infty} \frac{-i/n}{i/n} = -1.$$
Since these two limits do not agree, and since α is arbitrary, it follows that there are no points of $\mathbb{C}$ at which $f(z) = \overline{z}$ is differentiable.

1.9 (a) The fact that $\text{Re}\, z$ is constant along the imaginary axis, but variable parallel to the real axis, suggests that Re is not differentiable at i (or anywhere else for that matter). It also suggests looking at the sequences $z_n = i + i/n$ and $z'_n = i + 1/n$.

First let $z_n = i + i/n$; then
$$\lim_{n \to \infty} \frac{\text{Re}\, z_n - \text{Re}\, i}{z_n - i} = \lim_{n \to \infty} \frac{\text{Re}(i + i/n) - \text{Re}\, i}{(i + i/n) - i}$$
$$= \lim_{n \to \infty} \frac{0}{i/n} = \lim_{n \to \infty} 0 = 0.$$

Now let $z'_n = i + 1/n$; then
$$\lim_{n \to \infty} \frac{\text{Re}\, z'_n - \text{Re}\, i}{z'_n - i} = \lim_{n \to \infty} \frac{\text{Re}(i + 1/n) - \text{Re}\, i}{(i + 1/n) - i}$$
$$= \lim_{n \to \infty} \frac{1/n}{1/n} = 1.$$

Since these two limits do not agree, it follows that Re is not differentiable at i.

(b) f is a polynomial function: $f'(z) = 4z + 3$. Thus $f'(i) = 3 + 4i$.

(c) f is not differentiable at i, since it is not continuous at i.

1.10 To a close approximation, a small disc centred at i is mapped by f to a small disc centred at

$$f(i) = \frac{4i + 3}{2i^2 + 1} = -3 - 4i.$$

In the process the disc is scaled by the factor $|f'(i)|$ and rotated through the angle $\operatorname{Arg} f'(i)$.

By the Quotient Rule,

$$f'(z) = \frac{4(2z^2 + 1) - 4z(4z + 3)}{(2z^2 + 1)^2}$$

$$= \frac{-8z^2 - 12z + 4}{(2z^2 + 1)^2}.$$

So

$$f'(i) = \frac{-8i^2 - 12i + 4}{(2i^2 + 1)^2} = 12 - 12i.$$

This has modulus $12\sqrt{2}$ and principal argument $-\pi/4$.

So f has the effect of sending a small disc centred at i to a small disc centred at $-3 - 4i$. As it does so the disc is enlarged by the factor $12\sqrt{2}$ and rotated clockwise through the angle $\pi/4$.

Section 2

2.1 See Frame 1 (on page 17).

2.2 **(a)** Differentiating $v(x, y) = 3x^2y - y^3$ with respect to x while keeping y fixed, we obtain

$$\frac{\partial v}{\partial x}(x, y) = 6xy.$$

Differentiating v with respect to y while keeping x fixed, we obtain

$$\frac{\partial v}{\partial y}(x, y) = 3x^2 - 3y^2.$$

(b) So, at $(x, y) = (2, 1)$ the partial derivatives have the values

$$\frac{\partial v}{\partial x}(2, 1) = 12 \quad \text{and} \quad \frac{\partial v}{\partial y}(2, 1) = 9.$$

Notice that

$$\frac{\partial v}{\partial x}(2, 1) = -\frac{\partial u}{\partial y}(2, 1) \quad \text{and} \quad \frac{\partial v}{\partial y}(2, 1) = \frac{\partial u}{\partial x}(2, 1).$$

2.3 **(a)** Writing f in the form

$$f(x + iy) = u(x, y) + iv(x, y),$$

we obtain

$$f(x + iy) = e^x - ie^y.$$

So, in this case,

$$u(x, y) = e^x \quad \text{and} \quad v(x, y) = -e^y.$$

Hence

$$\frac{\partial u}{\partial x}(x, y) = e^x \quad \text{and} \quad \frac{\partial v}{\partial y}(x, y) = -e^y.$$

Since e^x is always positive, whereas $-e^y$ is always negative, the first of the Cauchy–Riemann equations fails to hold for each (x, y). It follows that f fails to be differentiable at all points of $\mathbb{C}$.

(b) Writing $f(z) = \bar{z}$ in the form

$$f(x + iy) = u(x, y) + iv(x, y),$$

we obtain

$$f(x + iy) = x - iy.$$

So, in this case,

$$u(x, y) = x \quad \text{and} \quad v(x, y) = -y.$$

Hence

$$\frac{\partial u}{\partial x}(x, y) = 1 \quad \text{and} \quad \frac{\partial v}{\partial y}(x, y) = -1.$$

It follows that the first of the Cauchy–Riemann equations fails to hold for each (x, y), and so f fails to be differentiable at all points of $\mathbb{C}$.

2.4 **(a)** Here $u(x, y) = x^3y - y\cos y$, so

$$\frac{\partial u}{\partial x}(x, y) = 3x^2y \quad \text{and} \quad \frac{\partial u}{\partial y}(x, y) = x^3 - \cos y + y\sin y.$$

So, at $(x, y) = (1, 0)$ the partial derivatives have the values

$$\frac{\partial u}{\partial x}(1, 0) = 0 \quad \text{and} \quad \frac{\partial u}{\partial y}(1, 0) = 0.$$

(b) Here $u(x, y) = ye^x - xy^3$, so

$$\frac{\partial u}{\partial x}(x, y) = ye^x - y^3 \quad \text{and} \quad \frac{\partial u}{\partial y}(x, y) = e^x - 3xy^2.$$

So, at $(x, y) = (1, 0)$ the partial derivatives have the values

$$\frac{\partial u}{\partial x}(1, 0) = 0 \quad \text{and} \quad \frac{\partial u}{\partial y}(1, 0) = e.$$

2.5 **(a)** From the trigonometric identities in *Unit A2*,

$$\sin(x + iy) = \sin x \cos iy + \cos x \sin iy$$
$$= \sin x \cosh y + i \cos x \sinh y,$$

so

$$u(x, y) = \sin x \cosh y \quad \text{and} \quad v(x, y) = \cos x \sinh y.$$

Hence

$$\frac{\partial u}{\partial x}(x, y) = \cos x \cosh y, \quad \frac{\partial v}{\partial x}(x, y) = -\sin x \sinh y,$$

$$\frac{\partial u}{\partial y}(x, y) = \sin x \sinh y, \quad \frac{\partial v}{\partial y}(x, y) = \cos x \cosh y.$$

These partial derivatives are defined and continuous on the whole of $\mathbb{C}$. Furthermore

$$\frac{\partial u}{\partial x}(x, y) = \frac{\partial v}{\partial y}(x, y) \quad \text{and} \quad \frac{\partial v}{\partial x}(x, y) = -\frac{\partial u}{\partial y}(x, y),$$

so the Cauchy–Riemann equations are satisfied at every point of $\mathbb{C}$.

By the Cauchy–Riemann Converse Theorem, $f(z) = \sin z$ is entire, and

$$f'(x + iy) = \frac{\partial u}{\partial x}(x, y) + i\frac{\partial v}{\partial x}(x, y)$$
$$= \cos x \cosh y - i \sin x \sinh y$$
$$= \cos x \cos iy - \sin x \sin iy$$
$$= \cos(x + iy).$$

Hence f' has domain $\mathbb{C}$ and $f'(z) = \cos z$. (You will see an easier way of finding this derivative in Section 3.)

(b) Here $f(x + iy) = |x + iy|^2 = x^2 + y^2$, so
$$u(x, y) = x^2 + y^2 \quad \text{and} \quad v(x, y) = 0.$$
Hence
$$\frac{\partial u}{\partial x}(x, y) = 2x, \quad \frac{\partial v}{\partial x}(x, y) = 0,$$
$$\frac{\partial u}{\partial y}(x, y) = 2y, \quad \frac{\partial v}{\partial y}(x, y) = 0.$$
The Cauchy–Riemann equations cannot be satisfied unless $2x = 0$ and $-2y = 0$, so f fails to be differentiable at all non-zero points of $\mathbb{C}$.

However, the Cauchy–Riemann equations *are* satisfied at $(0, 0)$ and the partial derivatives are defined on $\mathbb{C}$ and continuous (at $(0, 0)$), so by the Cauchy–Riemann Converse Theorem, f is differentiable at 0, and
$$f'(0) = \frac{\partial u}{\partial x}(0, 0) + i\frac{\partial v}{\partial x}(0, 0)$$
$$= 0 + i0$$
$$= 0.$$
Thus f' has domain $\{0\}$ and $f'(0) = 0$.

(This is the example, referred to in Section 1 (on page 7), of a function that is differentiable at a point, but not analytic at the point.)

Section 3

3.1 **(a)** Here $k = g \circ f$, where
$$g(z) = z^{900} \quad \text{and} \quad f(z) = z + 5.$$
Both f and g are entire, and
$$g'(z) = 900z^{899}, \quad f'(z) = 1.$$
So, by the Chain Rule, k is also entire and
$$k'(z) = g'(f(z))f'(z)$$
$$= 900(z + 5)^{899} \times 1 = 900(z + 5)^{899}.$$
(b) Here $k = g \circ f$, where
$$g(z) = \exp z \quad \text{and} \quad f(z) = z^2 + 4.$$
Both f and g are entire, and
$$g'(z) = \exp z, \quad f'(z) = 2z.$$
So, by the Chain Rule, k is also entire and
$$k'(z) = g'(f(z))f'(z) = 2z\exp(z^2 + 4).$$
(c) Here $k = g \circ f$, where
$$g(z) = \exp z \quad \text{and} \quad f(z) = \alpha z.$$
Both f and g entire, and
$$g'(z) = \exp z, \quad f'(z) = \alpha.$$
So, by the Chain Rule, k is also entire and
$$k'(z) = g'(f(z))f'(z) = \exp(\alpha z) \times \alpha = \alpha e^{\alpha z}.$$

3.2 The functions $z \longmapsto e^z$ and $z \longmapsto e^{-z}$ are entire with derivatives $z \longmapsto e^z$ and $z \longmapsto -e^{-z}$, respectively. It follows from the Combination Rules that:

(a) $f(z) = \sinh z = (e^z - e^{-z})/2$ is entire, and
$$f'(z) = \frac{(e^z - (-e^{-z}))}{2} = \frac{(e^z + e^{-z})}{2} = \cosh z;$$
(b) $f(z) = \cosh z = (e^z + e^{-z})/2$ is entire, and
$$f'(z) = \frac{(e^z - e^{-z})}{2} = \sinh z;$$

(c) $f(z) = \tanh z = \sinh z / \cosh z$ is analytic on its domain, and
$$f'(z) = \frac{\cosh z \times \cosh z - \sinh z \times \sinh z}{\cosh^2 z}$$
$$= \frac{1}{\cosh^2 z} = \operatorname{sech}^2 z.$$

3.3 **(a)** **(i)** Here $k = h \circ g \circ f$, where
$$h(z) = z^2, \quad g(z) = z^2 + 3 \quad \text{and} \quad f(z) = \sin z.$$
All of f, g and h are entire, and
$$h'(z) = 2z, \quad g'(z) = 2z \quad \text{and} \quad f'(z) = \cos z.$$
So, by the extended form of the Chain Rule, k is entire and
$$k'(z) = h'(g(f(z))) \times g'(f(z)) \times f'(z)$$
$$= 2(\sin^2 z + 3) \times 2\sin z \times \cos z$$
$$= 4\cos z(\sin^3 z + 3\sin z).$$
(ii) Here $k = h \circ g \circ f$, where
$$h(z) = \sin z, \quad g(z) = \exp z \quad \text{and} \quad f(z) = \cos(z) - z.$$
Now f, g and h are entire, and
$$h'(z) = \cos z, \quad g'(z) = \exp z \quad \text{and} \quad f'(z) = -\sin(z) - 1.$$
So, by the extended form of the Chain Rule, k is entire and
$$k'(z) = h'(g(f(z))) \times g'(f(z)) \times f'(z)$$
$$= \cos(\exp(\cos(z) - z)) \times \exp(\cos(z) - z)$$
$$\times (-\sin(z) - 1).$$
(iii) Here $k = h \circ g \circ f$, where
$$h(z) = \exp z, \quad g(z) = \frac{1}{z} + z \quad \text{and} \quad f(z) = \cos z.$$
The domain of k is $\mathbb{C} - \{(n + \frac{1}{2})\pi : n \in \mathbb{Z}\}$. Since this is a region, every point of the domain of k is a limit point of the domain. Furthermore, the functions f, g and h are differentiable, and
$$h'(z) = \exp z, \quad g'(z) = 1 - z^{-2} \quad \text{and} \quad f'(z) = -\sin z.$$
So, by the extended form of the Chain Rule, k is differentiable on its domain, and
$$k'(z) = h'(g(f(z))) \times g'(f(z)) \times f'(z)$$
$$= \exp((\cos z)^{-1} + \cos z) \times (1 - (\cos z)^{-2})$$
$$\times (-\sin z)$$
$$= \exp(\cos z + \sec z) \times (\tan z \sec z - \sin z).$$
(b) **(i)** k is differentiable on $\mathbb{C}$ and
$$k'(z) = \cos(\cosh z) \times \sinh z.$$
(ii) k is differentiable on $\mathbb{C}$ and
$$k'(z) = -\sin((1 + z)^{20}) \times 20(1 + z)^{19} \times 1$$
$$= -20(1 + z)^{19}\sin((1 + z)^{20}).$$
(iii) k is differentiable on $\mathbb{C}$ and
$$k'(z) = \exp(\exp(\sin z)) \times \exp(\sin z) \times \cos z.$$

3.4 By the Chain Rule,
$$f'(z) = i\,\mathrm{Log}'(1 + iz) = \frac{i}{1 + iz}.$$

To determine the domain of f', notice that the conditions of the Chain Rule are fulfilled at α provided that Log is differentiable at $1 + i\alpha$; that is, provided that $1 + i\alpha$ does not belong to the negative real axis (or 0). This means that $f'(\alpha)$ exists provided that α does not belong to $\{iy : y \geq 1\}$.

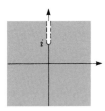

If α does belong to $\{iy : y \geq 1\}$, then $f'(\alpha)$ cannot exist because f is discontinuous at such values of α.

It follows that the domain of f' is $\mathbb{C} - \{iy : y \geq 1\}$.

3.5 The principal power functions in (a) and (b) can be differentiated using Corollary 2.

(a) $f'(z) = \pi z^{\pi - 1}$.

(b) $f'(z) = \frac{3}{2} z^{1/2}$. The domain of both these derivatives is the cut plane $\mathbb{C} - \{x \in \mathbb{R} : x \leq 0\}$.

By contrast, the integer power functions in (c) and (d) can be differentiated using the rule for differentiating integer powers given in Section 1.

(c) $f'(z) = 5z^4 \quad (z \in \mathbb{C})$.

(d) $f'(z) = -3z^{-4} \quad (z \neq 0)$.

3.6 With practice, the rules can be applied by inspection.

(a) $f'(z) = \left(e^z \times \dfrac{1}{z}\right) + (e^z \times \mathrm{Log}\,z)$

$\qquad = \left(\dfrac{1}{z} + \mathrm{Log}\,z\right) e^z \quad (z \in \mathbb{C} - \{x \in \mathbb{R} : x \leq 0\})$.

(b) $f'(z) = 20(z + \sin z)^{19}(1 + \cos z) \quad (z \in \mathbb{C})$.

(c) $f'(z) = 2\cos(z + \cosh z) \times (-\sin(z + \cosh z))$

$\qquad\qquad\qquad\qquad\qquad\qquad \times (1 + \sinh z)$

$\qquad = -(\sin(2z + 2\cosh z))(1 + \sinh z) \quad (z \in \mathbb{C})$.

(d) $f'(z) = \dfrac{(z \times 1/z) - (\mathrm{Log}\,z \times 1)}{z^2}$

$\qquad = \dfrac{1 - \mathrm{Log}\,z}{z^2} \quad (z \in \mathbb{C} - \{x \in \mathbb{R} : x \leq 0\})$.

Section 4

4.1 **(a)**

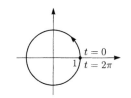

(b)

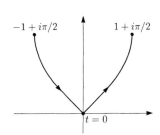

(c)

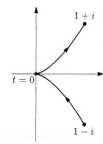

4.2 In each case treat t as if it were the complex variable z.

(a) Using the Restriction Rule, we obtain
$$\gamma'(t) = 1 - i \quad (t \in [-1, 2]).$$

In other words, the derivative is constant throughout the interval $[-1, 2]$. In particular, $\gamma'(0) = 1 - i$.

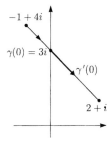

(b) Using the Restriction Rule, we obtain
$$\gamma'(t) = \cos' t + 2i\sin' t$$
$$= -\sin t + 2i\cos t \quad (t \in [0, 2\pi]).$$

In particular, $\gamma'(0) = 2i$.

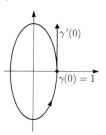

(c) Using the Restriction Rule, we obtain
$$\gamma'(t) = 2t + 2i \quad (t \in \mathbb{R}).$$
In particular, $\gamma'(0) = 2i$.

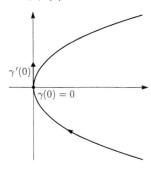

(d) Using the Restriction Rule, we obtain
$$\gamma'(t) = 2\cosh' t + 3i \sinh' t$$
$$= 2\sinh t + 3i \cosh t \quad (t \in \mathbb{R}).$$
In particular, $\gamma'(0) = 3i$.

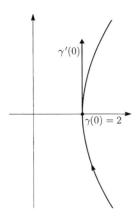

(e) Using the Restriction Rule, we obtain
$$\gamma'(t) = ie^{it} \quad (t \in [0, 2\pi]).$$
In particular, $\gamma'(0) = i$.

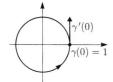

4.3 $\operatorname{Re}\gamma$ is differentiable on $[0, \infty[$, whereas $\operatorname{Im}\gamma$ is differentiable on $]0, \infty[$, but not at 0. It follows that γ is differentiable on $]0, \infty[$, but not at 0.

4.4 (a) This parametrization is differentiable and
$$\gamma'(t) = 1 + i \sin t \quad (t \in [0, 2\pi]).$$
Since $\gamma'(t)$ is continuous and non-zero on $[0, 2\pi]$, the parametrization is smooth.

(b) Here
$$\gamma'(t) = 2t - 2 \quad (t \in [0, 2]),$$
so $\gamma'(1) = 0$. Hence γ is *not* smooth.

(c) The real part of the parametrization is not differentiable at 0, and so the parametrization is not differentiable at 0. It follows that the parametrization is not smooth.

4.5 Consider the paths Γ_1 and Γ_2 with parametrizations
$$\gamma_1(t) = t \quad (t \in [0, 1]) \quad \text{and} \quad \gamma_2(t) = it \quad (t \in [0, 1]).$$
These paths are straight lines which intersect at right angles.

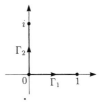

Under f they map to the paths with parametrizations
$$(f \circ \gamma_1)(t) = t^2 \quad (t \in [0, 1])$$
and
$$(f \circ \gamma_2)(t) = -t^2 \quad (t \in [0, 1]).$$
These image paths do not meet at right angles, since they both lie in the real axis.

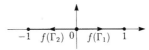

The above example does not contradict Theorem 4.2 for, although $f(z) = z^2$ is analytic at 0, $f'(0) = 0$.

4.6 As for Cartesian grids, polar grids consist of paths that intersect at right angles. It follows from Theorem 4.2 that if the analytic function has a derivative that is never zero, then the image of the polar grid consists of paths that meet at right angles.

SOLUTIONS TO THE EXERCISES

Section 1

1.1 $f(z) = 2z^2 + 5$ is defined on the whole of $\mathbb{C}$, so let $\alpha \in \mathbb{C}$. Then

$$
\begin{aligned}
f'(\alpha) &= \lim_{z \to \alpha} \frac{f(z) - f(\alpha)}{z - \alpha} \\
&= \lim_{z \to \alpha} \frac{(2z^2 + 5) - (2\alpha^2 + 5)}{z - \alpha} \\
&= \lim_{z \to \alpha} \frac{2(z^2 - \alpha^2)}{z - \alpha} \\
&= \lim_{z \to \alpha} 2(z + \alpha) \\
&= 4\alpha.
\end{aligned}
$$

Since α is an arbitrary complex number, f is differentiable on the whole of $\mathbb{C}$, and the derivative is the function

$$ f'(z) = 4z \quad (z \in \mathbb{C}). $$

1.2 Let $F = f/g$. Then

$$
\begin{aligned}
&\frac{F(z) - F(\alpha)}{z - \alpha} \\
&= \frac{f(z)/g(z) - f(\alpha)/g(\alpha)}{z - \alpha} \\
&= \frac{f(z)g(\alpha) - f(\alpha)g(z)}{(z - \alpha)g(z)g(\alpha)} \\
&= \frac{g(\alpha)(f(z) - f(\alpha)) - f(\alpha)(g(z) - g(\alpha))}{(z - \alpha)g(z)g(\alpha)} \\
&= \frac{g(\alpha)\left(\dfrac{f(z) - f(\alpha)}{z - \alpha}\right) - f(\alpha)\left(\dfrac{g(z) - g(\alpha)}{z - \alpha}\right)}{g(z)g(\alpha)}.
\end{aligned}
$$

Using the Combination Rules for limits, the continuity of g, and the fact that $g(\alpha) \neq 0$, we can take limits to obtain

$$ F'(\alpha) = \frac{g(\alpha)f'(\alpha) - f(\alpha)g'(\alpha)}{(g(\alpha))^2}. $$

1.3 **(a)** By the Combination Rules,

$$
\begin{aligned}
f'(z) &= \frac{(3z + 1)(2z + 2) - 3(z^2 + 2z + 1)}{(3z + 1)^2} \\
&= \frac{3z^2 + 2z - 1}{(3z + 1)^2}.
\end{aligned}
$$

The domain of f' is $\mathbb{C} - \{-1/3\}$.

(b) By the Combination Rules,

$$
\begin{aligned}
f'(z) &= \frac{(z^2 - z - 6)(3z^2) - (z^3 + 1)(2z - 1)}{(z^2 - z - 6)^2} \\
&= \frac{z^4 - 2z^3 - 18z^2 + 1}{(z^2 - z - 6)^2}.
\end{aligned}
$$

Since $z^2 - z - 6 = (z + 2)(z - 3)$, the domain of f' is $\mathbb{C} - \{-2, 3\}$.

(c) By the Reciprocal Rule,

$$ f'(z) = \frac{-(2z + 2)}{(z^2 + 2z + 2)^2}. $$

The roots of $z^2 + 2z + 2$ are $\dfrac{-2 \pm \sqrt{-4}}{2} = -1 \pm i$. The domain of f' is therefore $\mathbb{C} - \{-1 + i, -1 - i\}$.

(d) By the Sum Rule and the rule for differentiating integer powers,

$$ f'(z) = 2z + 5 - \frac{1}{z^2} - \frac{2}{z^3}. $$

The domain of f' is $\mathbb{C} - \{0\}$.

1.4 Arg is discontinuous at every point of the negative real axis. By Theorem 1.1, f is not differentiable at these points.

1.5 **(a)** Let $\alpha = a + ib$ be an arbitrary complex number. Let $z_n = (a + 1/n) + ib$; then $z_n \to \alpha$, and

$$
\begin{aligned}
\lim_{n \to \infty} \frac{\operatorname{Im} z_n - \operatorname{Im} \alpha}{z_n - \alpha} &= \lim_{n \to \infty} \frac{b - b}{1/n} \\
&= \lim_{n \to \infty} \frac{0}{1/n} = \lim_{n \to \infty} 0 = 0.
\end{aligned}
$$

Now let $z_n' = a + i(b + 1/n)$; then $z_n' \to \alpha$, and

$$
\begin{aligned}
\lim_{n \to \infty} \frac{\operatorname{Im} z_n' - \operatorname{Im} \alpha}{z_n' - \alpha} &= \lim_{n \to \infty} \frac{(b + 1/n) - b}{i/n} \\
&= \lim_{n \to \infty} \frac{1/n}{i/n} = -i.
\end{aligned}
$$

Since the two limits do not agree, it follows that Im fails to be differentiable at each point of $\mathbb{C}$.

(b) Let $\alpha = a + ib$ be an arbitrary complex number. Let $z_n = (a + 1/n) + ib$; then $z_n \to \alpha$, and

$$
\begin{aligned}
\lim_{n \to \infty} \frac{f(z_n) - f(\alpha)}{z_n - \alpha} &= \lim_{n \to \infty} \frac{(2(a + 1/n) + ib) - (2a + ib)}{1/n} \\
&= \lim_{n \to \infty} \frac{2/n}{1/n} = \lim_{n \to \infty} 2 = 2.
\end{aligned}
$$

Now let $z_n' = a + i(b + 1/n)$; then $z_n' \to \alpha$, and

$$
\begin{aligned}
\lim_{n \to \infty} \frac{f(z_n') - f(\alpha)}{z_n' - \alpha} &= \lim_{n \to \infty} \frac{(2a + i(b + 1/n)) - (2a + ib)}{i/n} \\
&= \lim_{n \to \infty} \frac{i/n}{i/n} = \lim_{n \to \infty} 1 = 1.
\end{aligned}
$$

Since the two limits do not agree, it follows that f fails to be differentiable at each point of $\mathbb{C}$.

1.6 To a close approximation, a small disc centred at 2 is mapped by f to small disc centred at $f(2) = -4$. In the process, the disc is scaled by the factor $|f'(2)|$ and rotated through the angle $\operatorname{Arg} f'(2)$.

By the Quotient Rule,

$$
\begin{aligned}
f'(z) &= \frac{3z^2(z - 6) - (z^3 + 8)}{(z - 6)^2} \\
&= \frac{2z^3 - 18z^2 - 8}{(z - 6)^2}.
\end{aligned}
$$

So

$$ f'(2) = -4. $$

This has modulus 4 and its principal argument is π.

So f has the effect of sending a small disc centered at 2 to a small disc centred at -4. As it does so, the disc is enlarged by the factor 4 and rotated anticlockwise through the angle π.

Section 2

2.1 (a) Differentiating $u(x,y) = 3x + xy + 2x^2y^2$ with respect to x while keeping y fixed, we obtain

$$\frac{\partial u}{\partial x}(x,y) = 3 + y + 4xy^2.$$

Differentiating with respect to y while keeping x fixed, we obtain

$$\frac{\partial u}{\partial y}(x,y) = x + 4x^2y.$$

(b) Here $u(x,y) = x\cos y + \exp(xy)$, so

$$\frac{\partial u}{\partial x}(x,y) = \cos y + y\exp(xy)$$

and

$$\frac{\partial u}{\partial y}(x,y) = -x\sin y + x\exp(xy).$$

(c) Here $u(x,y) = (x+y)^3$, so

$$\frac{\partial u}{\partial x}(x,y) = 3(x+y)^2 \quad \text{and} \quad \frac{\partial u}{\partial y}(x,y) = 3(x+y)^2.$$

2.2 Since $u(x,y) = x^2 + 2xy$, it follows that

$$\frac{\partial u}{\partial x}(x,y) = 2x + 2y \quad \text{and} \quad \frac{\partial u}{\partial y}(x,y) = 2x.$$

The slope of the graph at $(1,2)$ in the x-direction is

$$\frac{\partial u}{\partial x}(1,2) = 2 \times 1 + 2 \times 2 = 6.$$

The slope of the graph at $(1,2)$ in the y-direction is

$$\frac{\partial u}{\partial y}(1,2) = 2 \times 1 = 2.$$

2.3 Writing f in the form $f(x+iy) = u(x,y) + iv(x,y)$, we obtain

$$u(x,y) = e^x\sin y \quad \text{and} \quad v(x,y) = e^x\cos y.$$

Hence

$$\frac{\partial u}{\partial x}(x,y) = e^x\sin y, \quad \frac{\partial v}{\partial x}(x,y) = e^x\cos y,$$
$$\frac{\partial u}{\partial y}(x,y) = e^x\cos y, \quad \frac{\partial v}{\partial y}(x,y) = -e^x\sin y.$$

If f is differentiable at the point (x,y), then the Cauchy–Riemann equations require that

$$e^x\sin y = -e^x\sin y \quad \text{and} \quad e^x\cos y = -e^x\cos y;$$

that is,

$$e^x\sin y = 0 \quad \text{and} \quad e^x\cos y = 0.$$

But e^x is never zero, so $\sin y = \cos y = 0$, which is impossible. It follows that there is no point of $\mathbb{C}$ at which f is differentiable.

2.4 In this case $u(x,y) = x^2 + x - y^2$ and $v(x,y) = 2xy + y$, so

$$\frac{\partial u}{\partial x}(x,y) = 2x + 1, \quad \frac{\partial v}{\partial x}(x,y) = 2y,$$
$$\frac{\partial u}{\partial y}(x,y) = -2y, \quad \frac{\partial v}{\partial y}(x,y) = 2x + 1.$$

These partial derivatives are defined and continuous on the whole of $\mathbb{C}$. Furthermore

$$\frac{\partial u}{\partial x}(x,y) = \frac{\partial v}{\partial y}(x,y) \quad \text{and} \quad \frac{\partial v}{\partial x}(x,y) = -\frac{\partial u}{\partial y}(x,y),$$

so the Cauchy–Riemann equations are satisfied at every point of $\mathbb{C}$.

By Theorem 2.2, f is entire, and

$$f'(x+iy) = \frac{\partial u}{\partial x}(x,y) + i\frac{\partial v}{\partial x}(x,y) = (2x+1) + 2yi.$$

2.5 (a) Here $u(x,y) = x^2 + y^2$ and $v(x,y) = x^2 - y^2$, so

$$\frac{\partial u}{\partial x}(x,y) = 2x, \quad \frac{\partial v}{\partial x}(x,y) = 2x,$$
$$\frac{\partial u}{\partial y}(x,y) = 2y, \quad \frac{\partial v}{\partial y}(x,y) = -2y.$$

The Cauchy–Riemann equations are satisfied only if $x = -y$. So f cannot be differentiable at (x,y) unless $x = -y$. Since the above partial derivatives exist, and are continuous on $\mathbb{C}$ (and in particular when $x = -y$), it follows from Theorem 2.2 that f is differentiable on the set $\{(x,y) : x = -y\}$.

On this set,

$$f'(x,y) = \frac{\partial u}{\partial x}(x,y) + i\frac{\partial v}{\partial x}(x,y) = 2x + 2xi = 2x(1+i).$$

(b) Here $u(x,y) = xy$ and $v(x,y) = 0$, so

$$\frac{\partial u}{\partial x}(x,y) = y, \quad \frac{\partial v}{\partial x}(x,y) = 0,$$
$$\frac{\partial u}{\partial y}(x,y) = x, \quad \frac{\partial v}{\partial y}(x,y) = 0.$$

The Cauchy–Riemann equations are not satisfied unless $y = -x = 0$. So f is not differentiable, except possibly at 0. Since the above partial derivatives exist, and are continuous at $(0,0)$, it follows from Theorem 2.2 that f is differentiable at 0. Furthermore

$$f'(0,0) = \frac{\partial u}{\partial x}(0,0) + i\frac{\partial v}{\partial x}(0,0) = 0.$$

Section 3

3.1 (a) By the Reciprocal Rule,

$$\operatorname{sech}' z = \frac{-\sinh z}{\cosh^2 z} = -\operatorname{sech} z \tanh z.$$

(b) By the Reciprocal Rule,

$$\operatorname{cosech}' z = \frac{-\cosh z}{\sinh^2 z} = -\operatorname{cosech} z \coth z.$$

(c) By the Quotient Rule,

$$\coth' z = \frac{\sinh^2 z - \cosh^2 z}{\sinh^2 z} = \frac{-1}{\sinh^2 z} = -\operatorname{cosech}^2 z.$$

3.2 The function $z \longmapsto z + 1$ is entire with derivative $z \longmapsto 1$. Since Log is differentiable on the cut plane $\mathbb{C} - \{x \in \mathbb{R} : x \leq 0\}$ and $z + 1$ lies in the cut plane whenever $z \in \mathbb{C} - \{x \in \mathbb{R} : x \leq -1\}$, it follows that $z \longmapsto \operatorname{Log}(z + 1)$ is differentiable on $\mathbb{C} - \{x \in \mathbb{R} : x \leq -1\}$, with derivative $z \longmapsto \dfrac{1}{z+1}$, by the Chain Rule.

Since exp is entire, $z \longmapsto \exp(z^2)$ is differentiable on $\mathbb{C}$ with derivative $z \longmapsto 2z\exp(z^2)$, by the Chain Rule.

It follows from the Sum Rule that f is differentiable on $\mathbb{C} - \{x \in \mathbb{R} : x \leq -1\}$, with derivative

$$f'(z) = \frac{1}{z+1} + 2z\exp(z^2).$$

Now f is not differentiable on $\{x \in \mathbb{R} : x \leq -1\}$ because it is discontinuous at points of this set. The domain of f' is therefore $\mathbb{C} - \{x \in \mathbb{R} : x \leq -1\}$. Note that this domain does not include all points at which $\dfrac{1}{z+1} + 2z\exp(z^2)$ is defined.

3.3 (a) $f'(z) = -(\sin z + 1) \times \cos(\cos z - z)$

(b) $f'(z) = 2z^2 \exp(z^2 + i) + \exp(z^2 + i) - \sin z$

(c) $f'(z) = \dfrac{\exp(z+1)(1/z) - \text{Log}(z)\exp(z+1)}{(\exp(z+1))^2}$

$\qquad = \dfrac{(1/z) - \text{Log}\, z}{\exp(z+1)}$

(d) $f'(z) = -\sin(3\sin(i + \tan z)) \times 3\cos(i + \tan z)$

$\qquad\qquad\qquad\qquad\qquad\qquad \times \sec^2 z$

Section 4

4.1 (a) Using the Restriction Rule, we obtain

$\gamma'(t) = (2t + i)\exp(t^2 + it) \quad (t \in [-1, 1])$.

(b) Using the Restriction Rule, we obtain

$\gamma'(t) = 2t - i\sin t \quad (t \in [0, 2])$.

(c) Using the Restriction Rule, we obtain

$\gamma'(t) = -5\sin t + 7i\cos t \quad (t \in [-\pi, \pi])$.

(d) Because there are no points of its domain at which the complex modulus function is differentiable we cannot apply the Restriction Rule to γ (as given). Instead we use Theorem 4.1.

Since $\phi : t \longmapsto |t| \; (t \in [-1, 1])$ is differentiable everywhere except at 0 and $\psi : t \longmapsto t^4 + t \; (t \in [-1, 1])$ is differentiable everywhere, it follows from Theorem 4.1, that

$\gamma'(t) = \begin{cases} -1 + (4t^3 + 1)i, & t \in [-1, 0[, \\ 1 + (4t^3 + 1)i, & t \in]0, 1]. \end{cases}$

4.2 (a) This parametrization is differentiable on the whole of its domain $I = [-1, 1]$. Furthermore, the derivative is continuous and non-zero on I, so the parametrization is smooth.

(b) The derivative of this parametrization is zero when $t = 0$, so the parametrization is not smooth.

(c) This parametrization is differentiable on the whole of its domain $I = [-\pi, \pi]$. Furthermore, the derivative is continuous and non-zero on I, so the parametrization is smooth.

(d) This parametrization is not differentiable when $t = 0$ so the parametrization is not smooth.

4.3 (a) The paths meet at i since $\gamma_1(0) = \gamma_2(1) = i$. Now

$\gamma_1'(t) = 2\cos t + i \quad \text{and} \quad \gamma_2'(t) = -1 + 2it$,

so

$\gamma_1'(0) = 2 + i \quad \text{and} \quad \gamma_2'(1) = -1 + 2i$.

The angle from Γ_1 to Γ_2 at i is given by

$\begin{aligned} \text{Arg}\left(\frac{\gamma_2'(1)}{\gamma_1'(0)}\right) &= \text{Arg}\left(\frac{-1 + 2i}{2 + i}\right) \\ &= \text{Arg}\left(\tfrac{1}{5}(-1 + 2i)(\overline{2 + i})\right) \\ &= \text{Arg}((-1 + 2i)(2 - i)) \\ &= \text{Arg}\, 5i = \pi/2. \end{aligned}$

(b) Since $f'(z) = 2\sin z \cos z = \sin(2z)$, we have

$f'(i) = \sin(2i) \neq 0$.

Hence f is conformal at i (by Theorem 4.2), and so the angle from $f(\Gamma_1)$ to $f(\Gamma_2)$ at $f(i)$ is the same as the angle from Γ_1 to Γ_2 at i, namely $\pi/2$.